SPMG

NHM

New Heinemann Maths

Answer Book

Contents

Heinemann

Heinemann Educational Publishers
Halley Court, Jordan Hill, Oxford, OX2 8EJ
a division of Reed Educational & Professional Publishing Ltd
www.heinemann.co.uk

ISBN 0 435 17207 7

First published 2000

04
10 9 8 7 6 5 4

Designed by Gecko Limited, Bicester, Oxon.

Printed and bound in Great Britain

1

Count in threes. Colour.

1	2	**3**	4	5	**6**	7	8	**9**	10	11	**12**
											13
29	**30**	31	32	**33**	34	35	**36**				14
28											**15**
27	26	25	**24**	23	22	**21**	20	19	**18**	17	16

Colour odd numbers red.

1	2	3	4	5	6
16	17	18	19	20	7
15	24	23	22	21	8
14	13	12	11	10	9

Colour even numbers blue.

20	25	30	35	40	45
21	26	31	36	41	46
22	27	32	37	42	47
23	28	33	38	43	48
24	29	34	39	44	49

How many altogether?

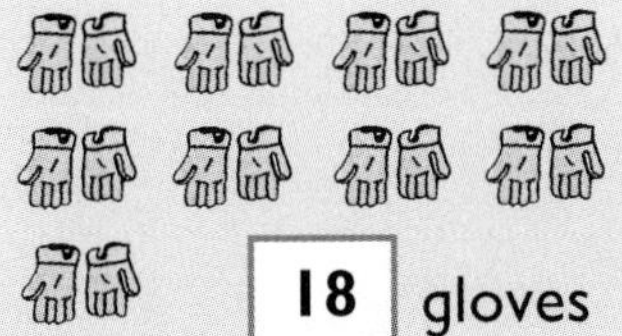

18 gloves

24 flowers

Count in twos from

20 to 36 | 25 to 43 | 50 to 30

Count in threes from

0 to 24 | 15 to 36 | 21 to 0

2

How many altogether?

25 flowers

16 flowers

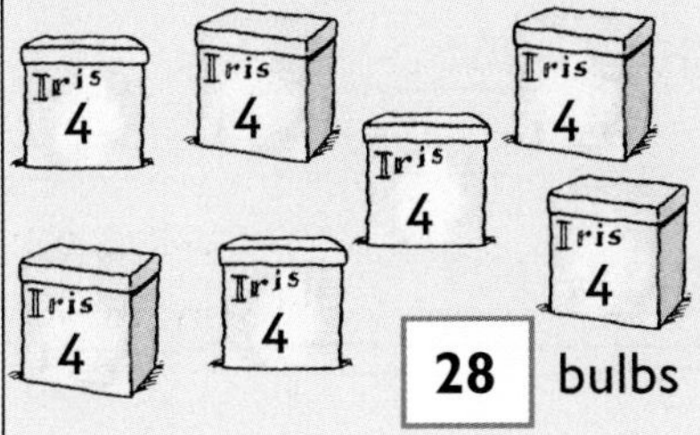

28 bulbs

50 bulbs

Complete.

0	5	10	**15**	**20**	25	**30**	35	**40**	**45**	**50**
0	4	**8**	**12**	16	**20**	**24**	**28**	**32**	36	**40**
50	45	**40**	**35**	**30**	25	20	15	**10**	**5**	**0**
40	**36**	**32**	28	24	20	**16**	**12**	8	**4**	**0**

Count in fives from

0 to 30 | 25 to 50 | 50 to 30 | 35 to 10

Count in fours from

0 to 24 | 16 to 40 | 48 to 32 | 36 to 8

3

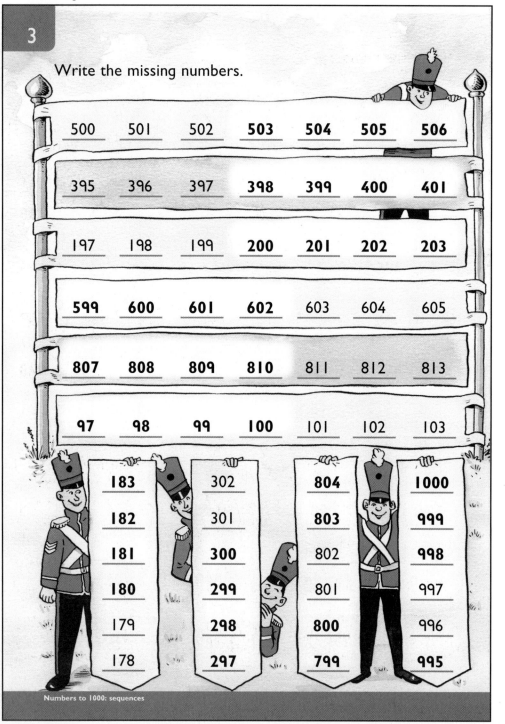

Write the missing numbers.

500	501	502	**503**	**504**	**505**	**506**
395	396	397	**398**	**399**	**400**	**401**
197	198	199	**200**	**201**	**202**	**203**
599	**600**	**601**	**602**	603	604	605
807	**808**	**809**	**810**	811	812	813
97	**98**	**99**	**100**	101	102	103

183	302	**804**	**1000**
182	301	**803**	**999**
181	**300**	802	**998**
180	**299**	801	997
179	**298**	**800**	996
178	**297**	**799**	**995**

4

Colour red the number

after 364 **365** | after 270 **271** | after 499 **500** | after 550 **551**

Colour yellow the number

before 693 **692** | before 950 **949** | before 716 **715** | before 500 **499**

Colour blue the number

after 823 **824** | before 100 **99** | after 866 **867** | before 1000 **999**

Write the number after

657 **658** 291 **292** 804 **805** 699 **700**

Write the number before

514 **513** 327 **326** 800 **799** 311 **310**

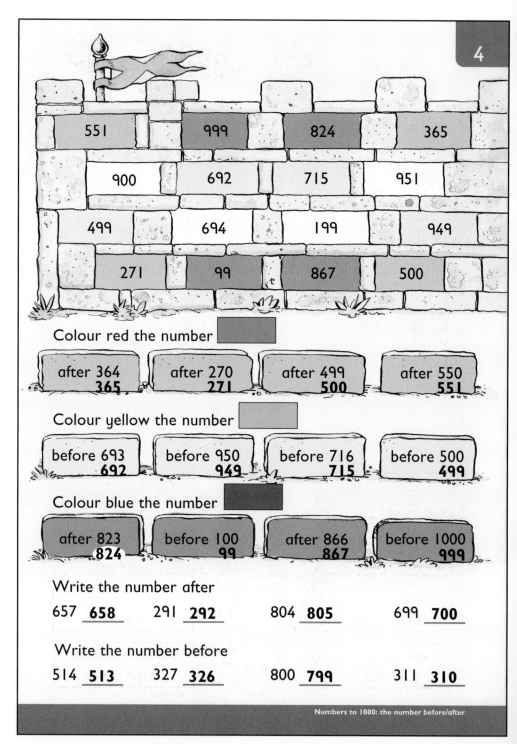

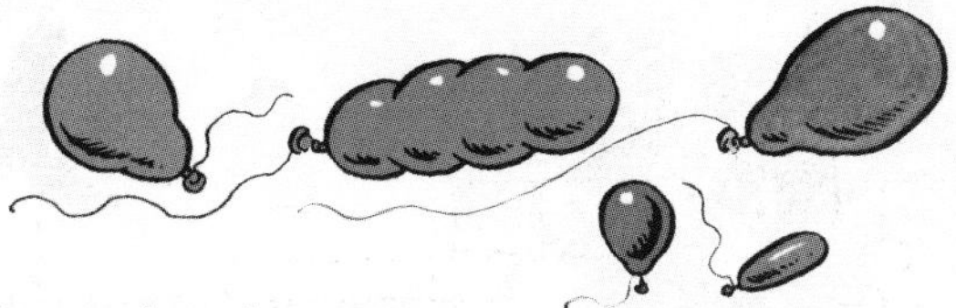

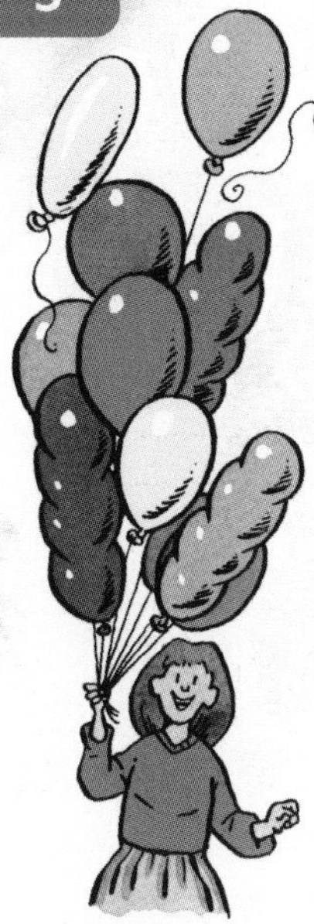

Write the number between

156 and 158	**157**	732 and 734	**733**
981 and 983	**982**	218 and 220	**219**
847 and 845	**846**	470 and 468	**469**
527 and 529	**528**	801 and 799	**800**
111 and 109	**110**	749 and 751	**750**
299 and 301	**300**	1000 and 998	**999**

Write the numbers between

198 **199** **200** 201

402 **401** **400** **399** 398

Match.

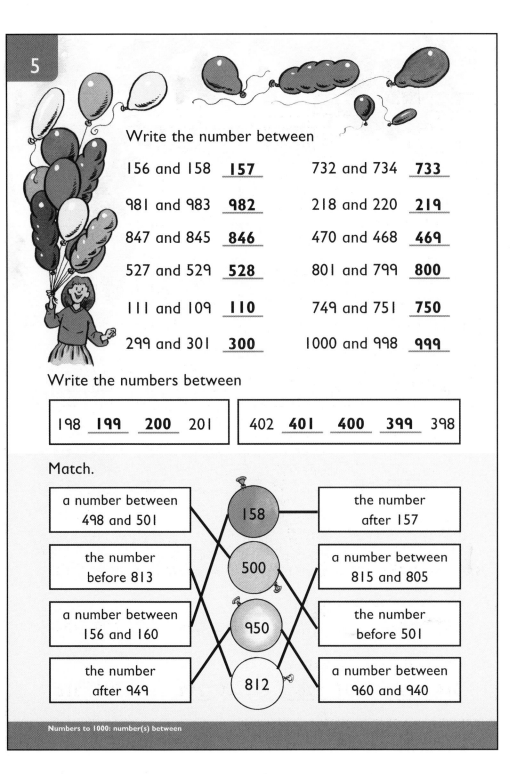

a number between 498 and 501	158	the number after 157
the number before 813	500	a number between 815 and 805
a number between 156 and 160	950	the number before 501
the number after 949	812	a number between 960 and 940

Write the number

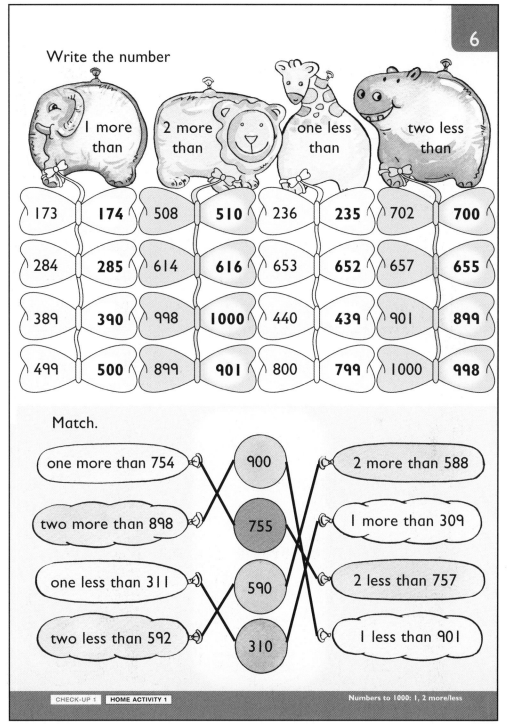

1 more than		2 more than		one less than		two less than	
173	**174**	508	**510**	236	**235**	702	**700**
284	**285**	614	**616**	653	**652**	657	**655**
389	**390**	998	**1000**	440	**439**	901	**899**
499	**500**	899	**901**	800	**799**	1000	**998**

Match.

one more than 754	900	2 more than 588
two more than 898	755	1 more than 309
one less than 311	590	2 less than 757
two less than 592	310	1 less than 901

7

Complete.

130	**360**	650	**307**	743	**902**
120	**350**	640	**297**	733	**892**
110	**340**	630	**287**	723	882
100	**330**	**620**	**277**	**713**	872
90	320	**610**	267	**703**	862
80	310	**600**	257	**693**	**852**
70	300	**590**	247	**683**	**842**

Write the number **10 more than**

Write the number **ten less than**

8

Complete.

400	500	600	**700**	**800**	**900**	**1000**
0	**100**	**200**	**300**	400	500	600
260	360	460	**560**	**660**	**760**	**860**

130	**230**	**330**	**430**	530	630	730
343	**443**	543	643	743	**843**	**943**
55	**155**	255	355	455	**555**	**655**

650	700	750	**800**	**850**	**900**	**950**
50	**100**	**150**	**200**	250	300	350

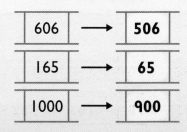

Write the number

one hundred more than

807	→	**907**
478	→	**578**
900	→	**1000**

100 less than

606	→	**506**
165	→	**65**
1000	→	**900**

9

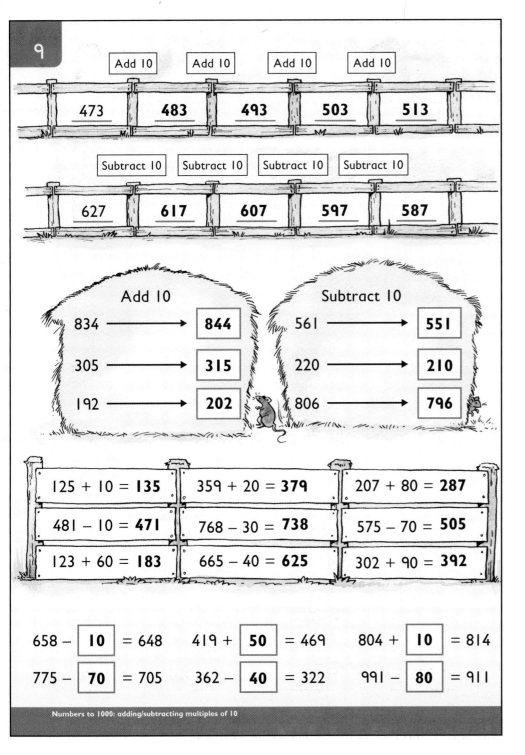

Add 10 | Add 10 | Add 10 | Add 10

473 → **483** → **493** → **503** → **513**

Subtract 10 | Subtract 10 | Subtract 10 | Subtract 10

627 → **617** → **607** → **597** → **587**

Add 10

834 → **844**

305 → **315**

192 → **202**

Subtract 10

561 → **551**

220 → **210**

806 → **796**

125 + 10 = **135**	359 + 20 = **379**	207 + 80 = **287**
481 – 10 = **471**	768 – 30 = **738**	575 – 70 = **505**
123 + 60 = **183**	665 – 40 = **625**	302 + 90 = **392**

658 – **10** = 648	419 + **50** = 469	804 + **10** = 814
775 – **70** = 705	362 – **40** = 322	991 – **80** = 911

10

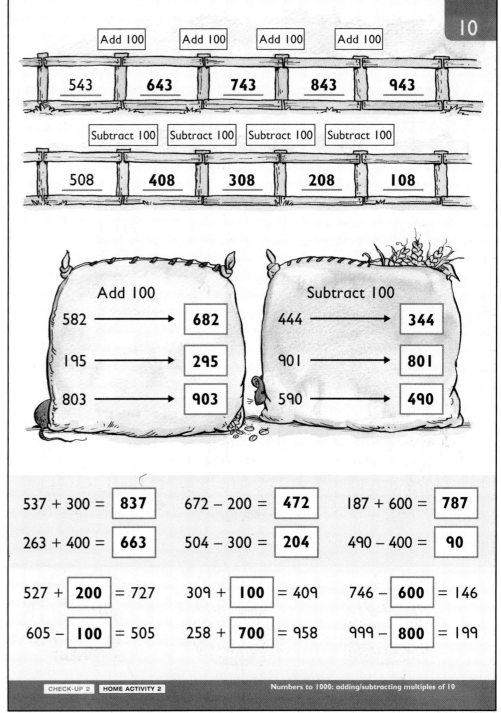

Add 100 | Add 100 | Add 100 | Add 100

543 → **643** → **743** → **843** → **943**

Subtract 100 | Subtract 100 | Subtract 100 | Subtract 100

508 → **408** → **308** → **208** → **108**

Add 100

582 → **682**

195 → **295**

803 → **903**

Subtract 100

444 → **344**

901 → **801**

590 → **490**

537 + 300 = **837**	672 – 200 = **472**	187 + 600 = **787**
263 + 400 = **663**	504 – 300 = **204**	490 – 400 = **90**

527 + **200** = 727	309 + **100** = 409	746 – **600** = 146
605 – **100** = 505	258 + **700** = 958	999 – **800** = 199

11

How many?

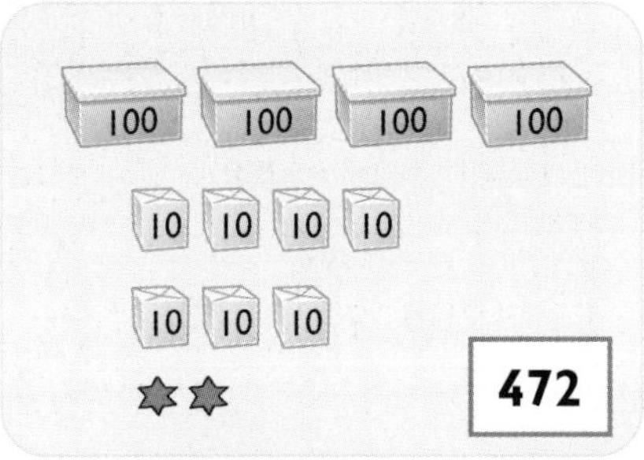

472

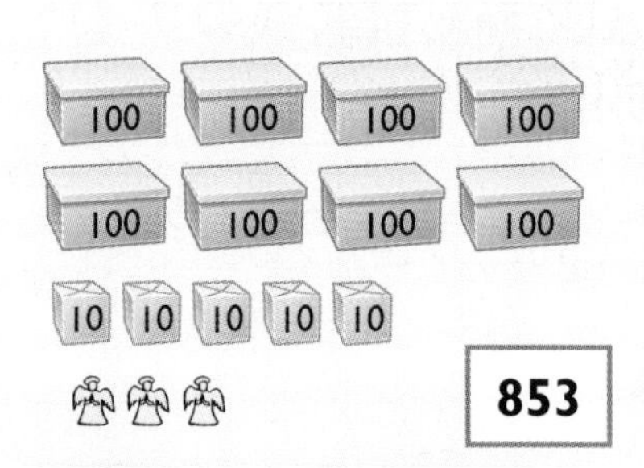

853

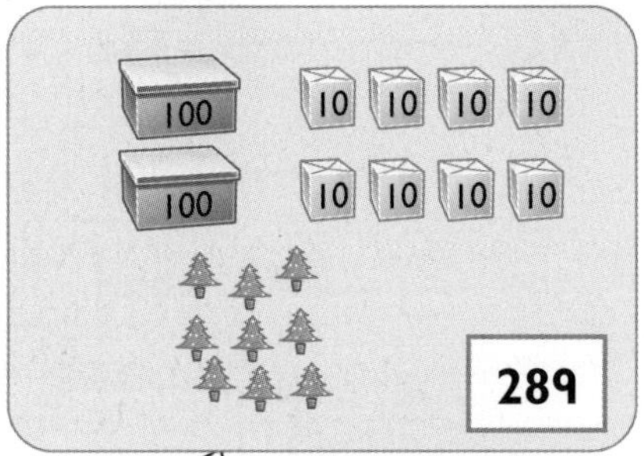

289

666

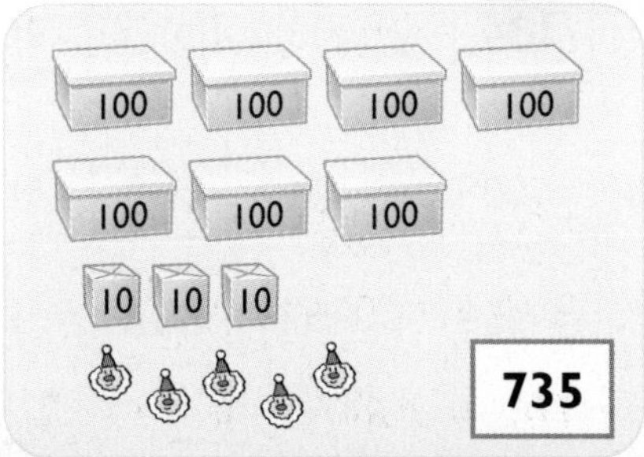

735

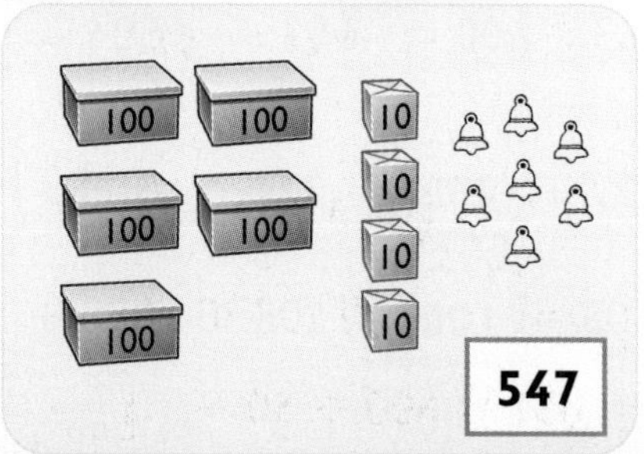

547

12

How many pence?

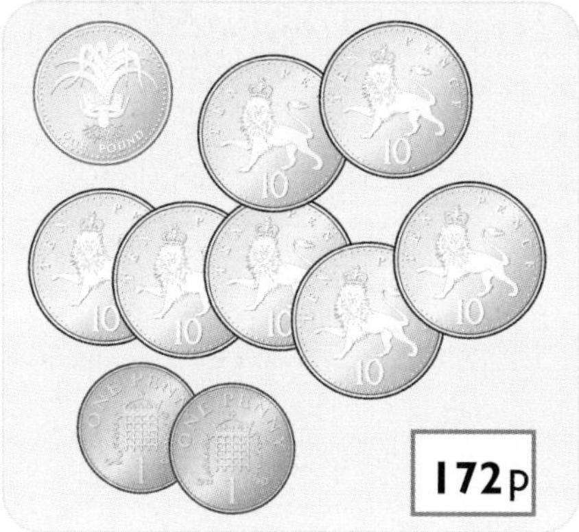
172 p

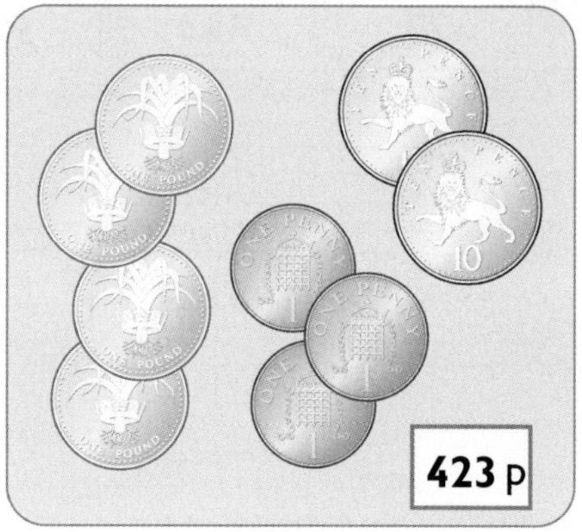
423 p

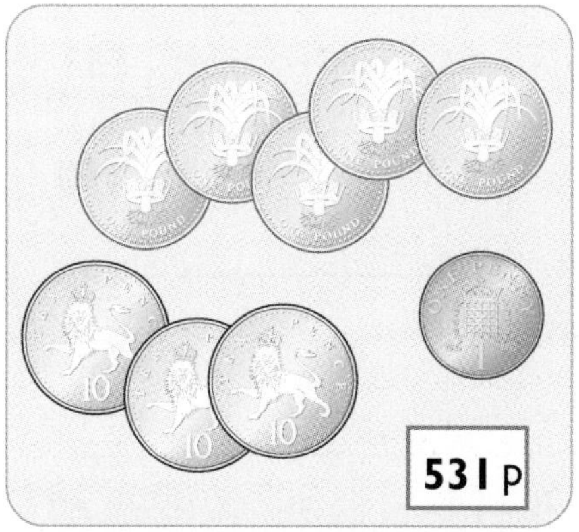
531 p

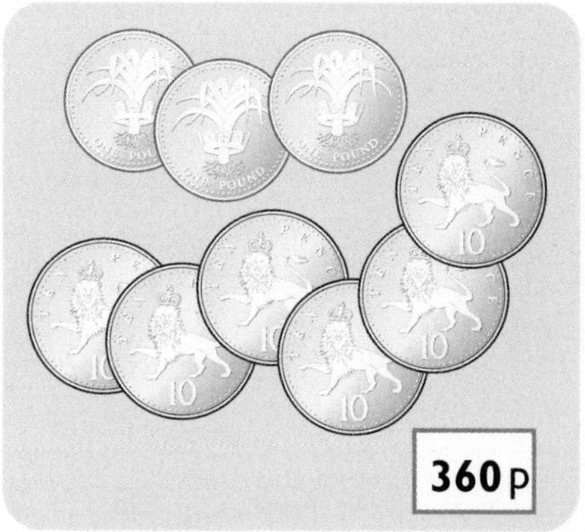
360 p

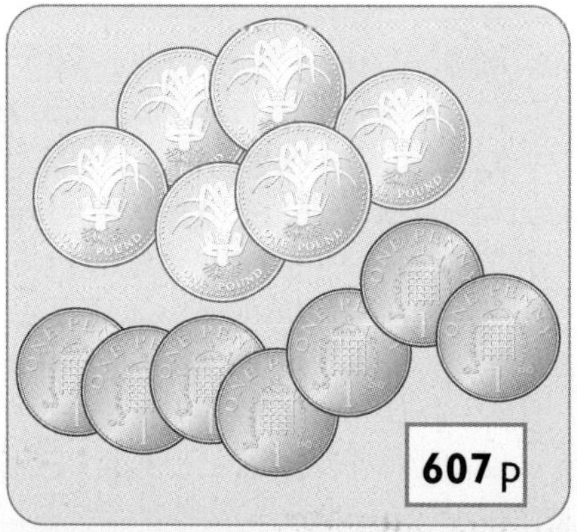
607 p

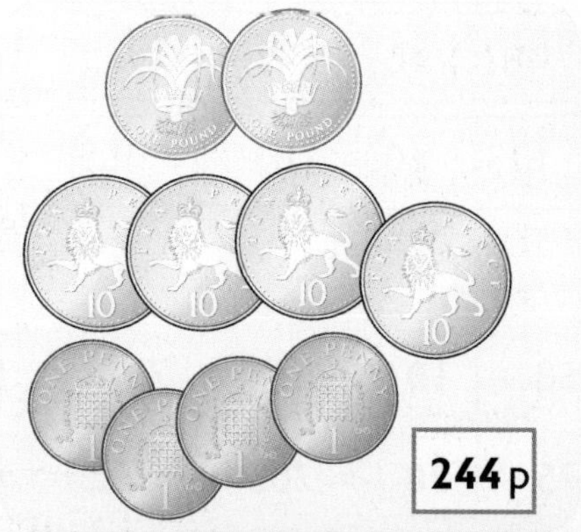
244 p

13

How many?

158

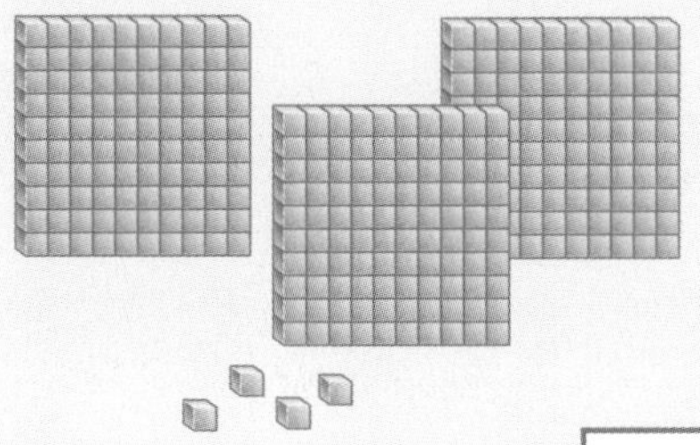

✓ **304**

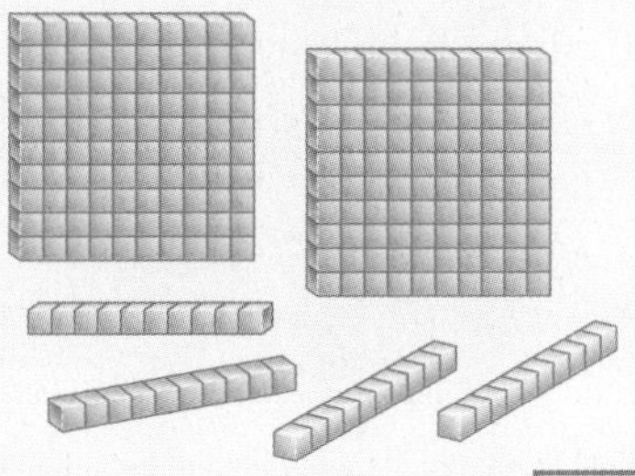

240

Tick (✓) the larger number.

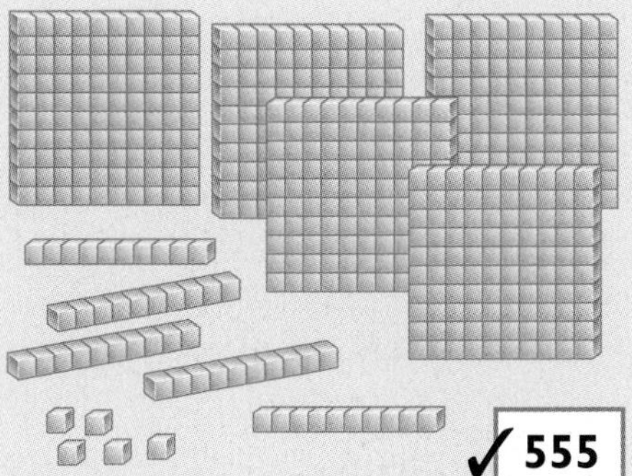

✓ **555**

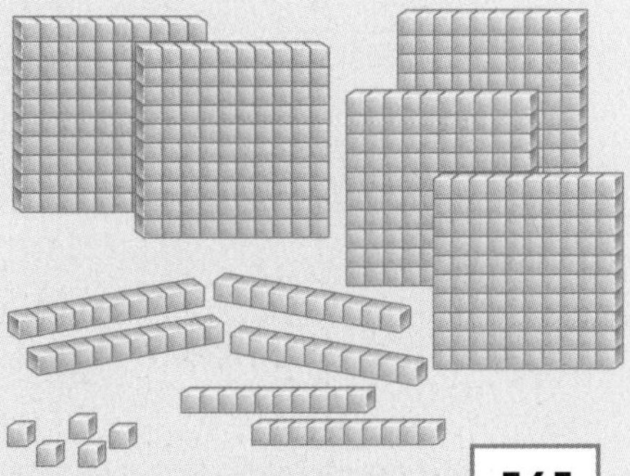

565

Tick (✓) the smaller number.

14

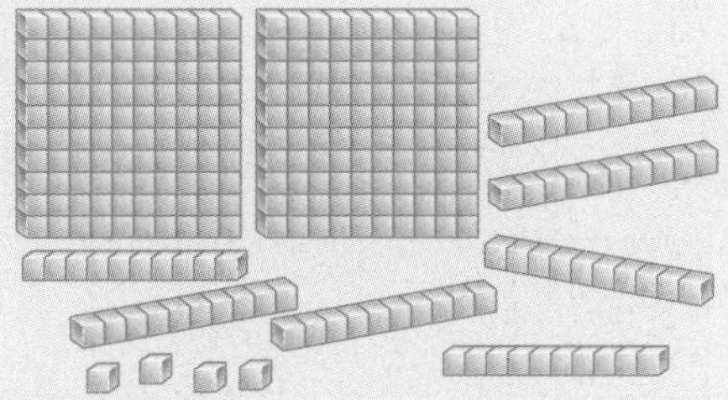

2 hundreds 7 tens and 4 units

200 + 70 + **4** = **274**

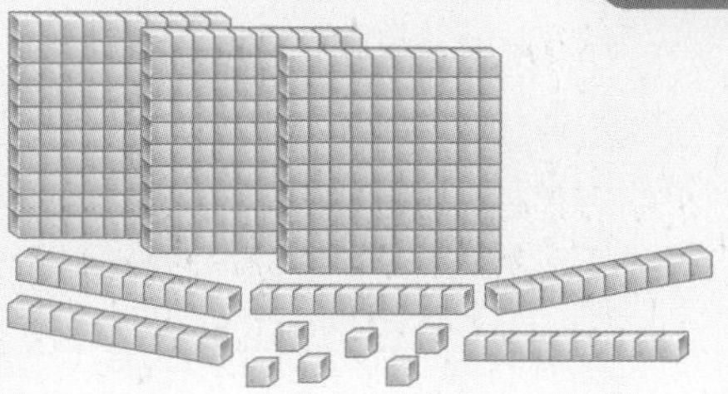

3 hundreds **5** tens and **6** units

300 + **50** + **6** = **356**

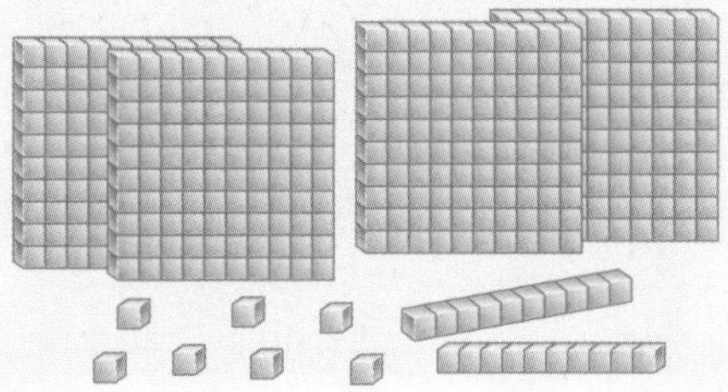

4 hundreds **2** tens and **7** units

400 + **20** + **7** = **427**

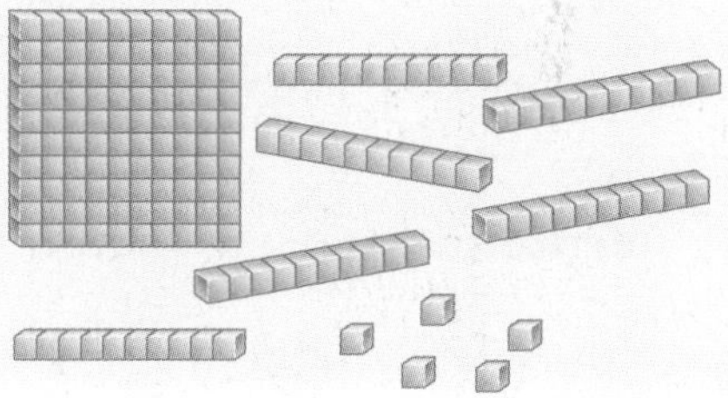

1 hundreds **6** tens and **5** units

100 + **60** + **5** = **165**

500 + 30 + 5 = **535**

900 + 20 + 9 = **929**

700 + 0 + 3 = **703**

157 = **100** + **50** + **7**

481 = **400** + **80** + **1**

690 = **600** + **90** + **0**

427 = 400 + **20** + 7

293 = **200** + 90 + 3

651 = 600 + 50 + **1**

865 = **800** + 60 + 5

349 = 300 + **40** + 9

702 = 700 + **0** + **2**

15

Colour the numbers with
- 2 hundreds blue
- 5 tens green
- 3 units red.

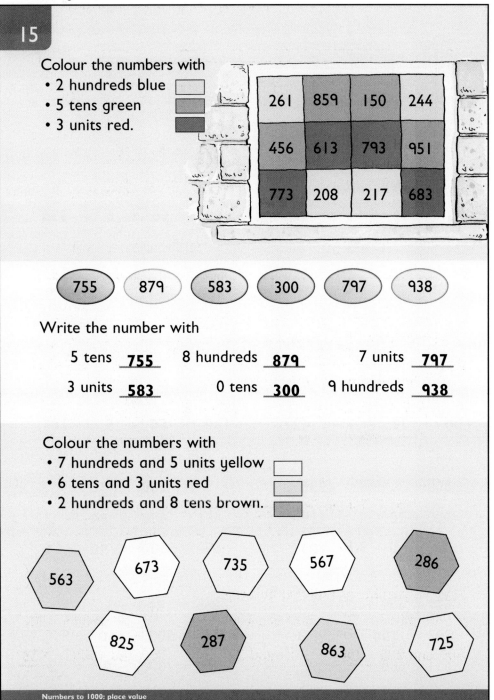

261	859	150	244
456	613	793	951
773	208	217	683

755 879 583 300 797 938

Write the number with

5 tens **755** 8 hundreds **879** 7 units **797**

3 units **583** 0 tens **300** 9 hundreds **938**

Colour the numbers with
- 7 hundreds and 5 units yellow
- 6 tens and 3 units red
- 2 hundreds and 8 tens brown.

563 673 735 567 286

825 287 863 725

16

Tick (✓) the larger number.

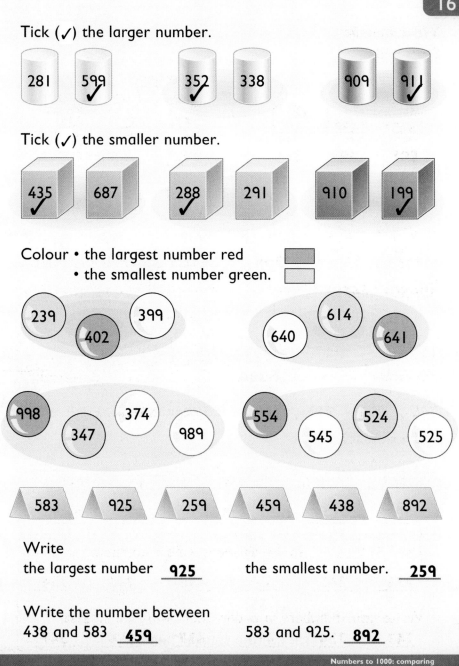

281 599 ✓ 352 ✓ 338 909 911 ✓

Tick (✓) the smaller number.

435 ✓ 687 288 ✓ 291 910 199 ✓

Colour
- the largest number red
- the smallest number green.

239 402 399 640 614 641

998 347 374 989 554 545 524 525

583 925 259 459 438 892

Write

the largest number **925** the smallest number. **259**

Write the number between

438 and 583 **459** 583 and 925. **892**

17

Write in order.
Start with

the smallest

591 **598** **638**

the largest

762 **627** **267**

the longest

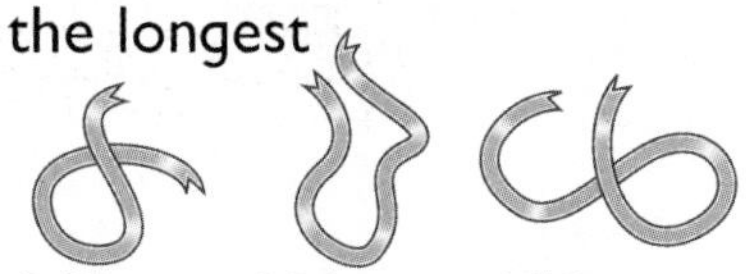

143 cm 121 cm 132 cm

143 cm **132 cm** **121 cm**

the shortest

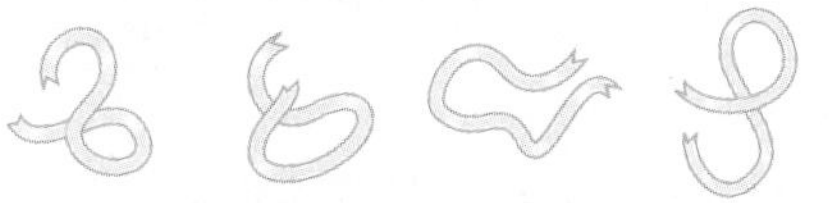

683 cm 386 cm 638 cm 368 cm

368 cm **386 cm** **638 cm** **683 cm**

the lightest

745 g **754 g** **903 g** **930 g**

the heaviest

552 g **525 g** **255 g** **225 g**

the smallest.

475 **676** **677** **757** **767**

Use 3 7 4 to make different 3-digit numbers.

374 **347** **437** **473** **743** **734**

Write your numbers in order. Start with the largest.

743 **734** **473** **437** **374** **347**

18

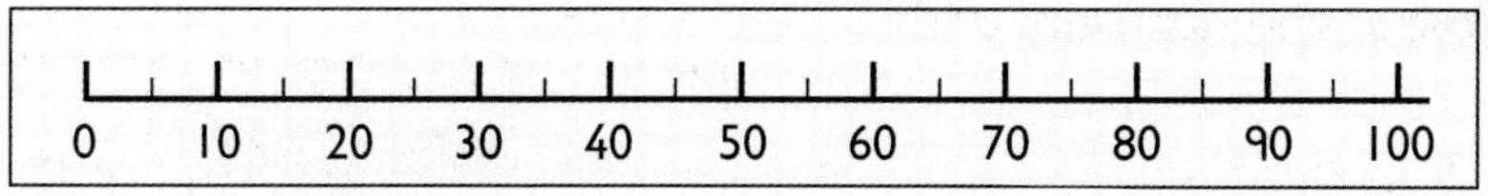

What number is halfway between

20 and 30 **25** 70 and 80 **75**

0 and 10 **5** 100 and 90? **95**

What number is halfway between

30 and 50 **40** 80 and 100? **90**

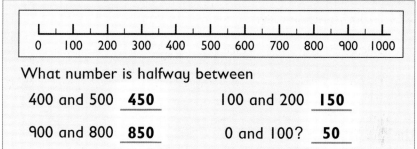

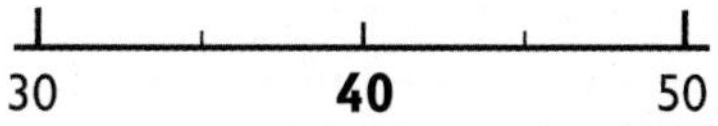

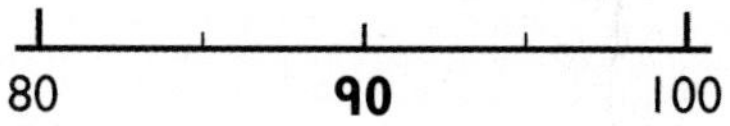

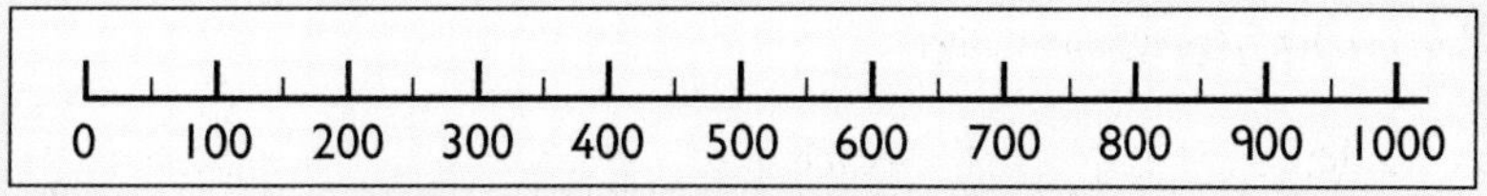

What number is halfway between

400 and 500 **450** 100 and 200 **150**

900 and 800 **850** 0 and 100? **50**

What number is halfway between

700 and 900 **800** 600 and 800? **700**

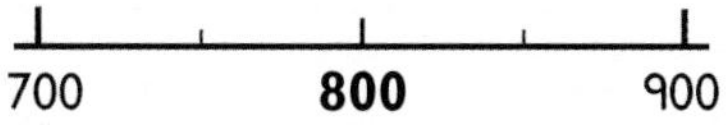

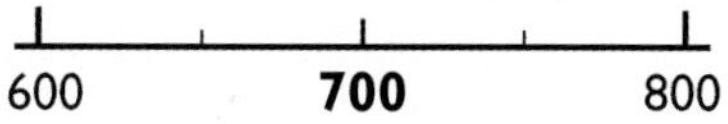

What number is halfway between

40 and 60 **50** 600 and 700 **650** 50 and 60 **55**

400 and 200 **300** 10 and 30 **20** 900 and 1000? **950**

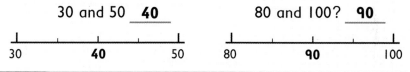

19

Colour the balloon

at 5

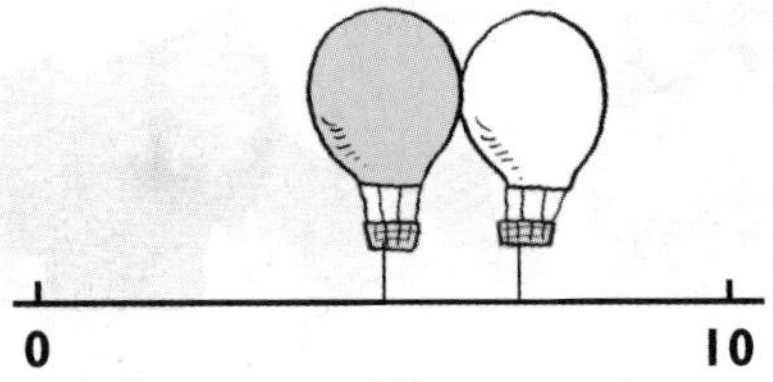

at 22

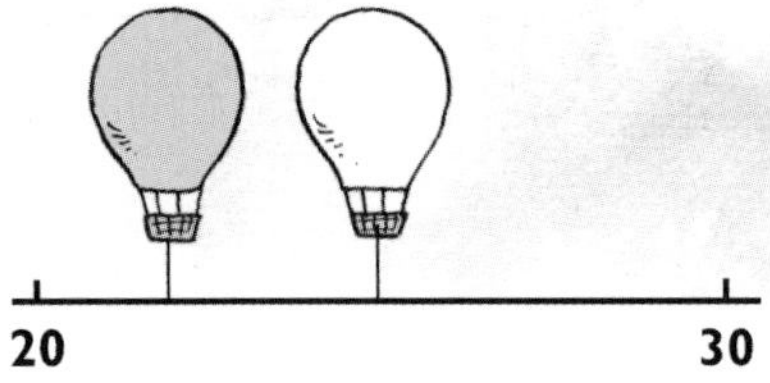

at 46

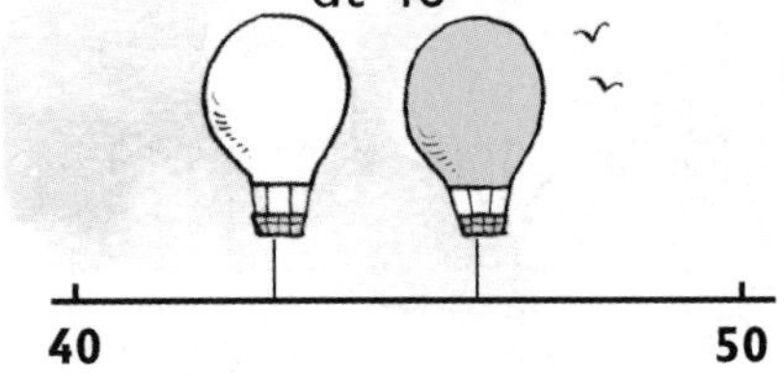

at 78.

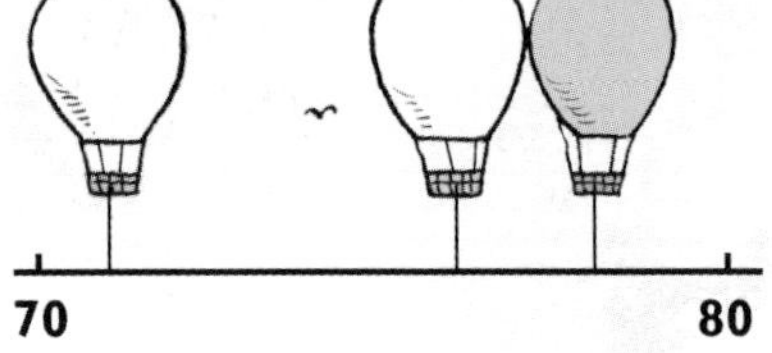

Match.

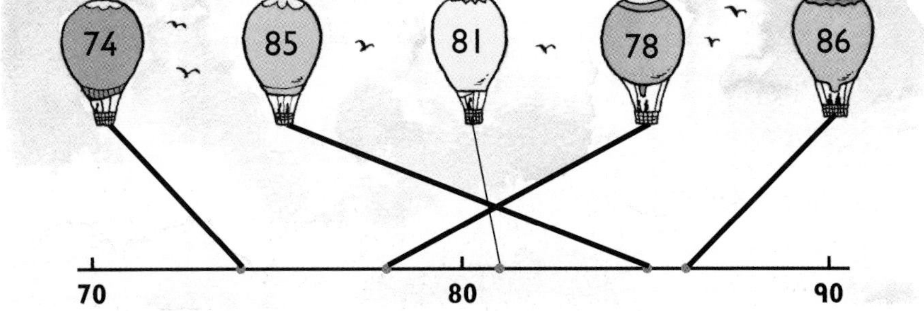

Write the number on each balloon.

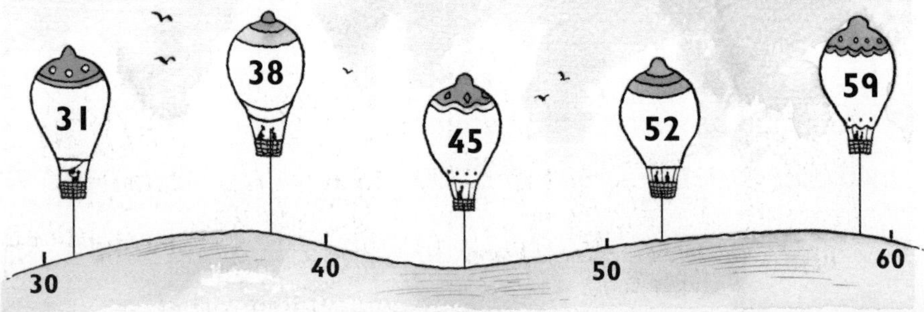

20

Colour the numbers

nearer to 10 than 20

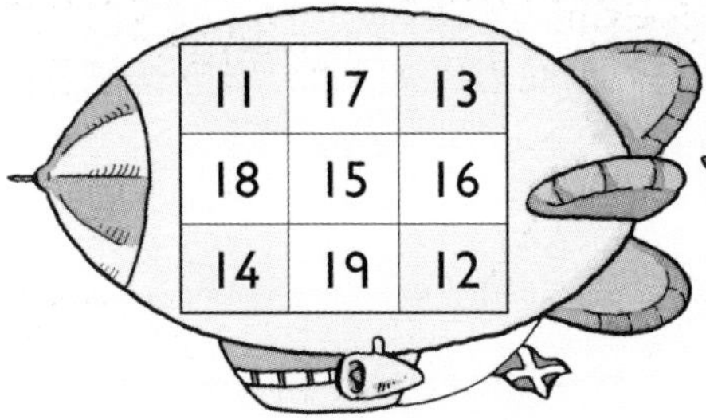

11	17	13
18	15	16
14	19	12

nearer to 30 than 20

25	24	21
22	26	23
29	28	27

nearer to 30 than 40

38	32	35
34	36	33
37	31	39

nearer to 40 than 50.

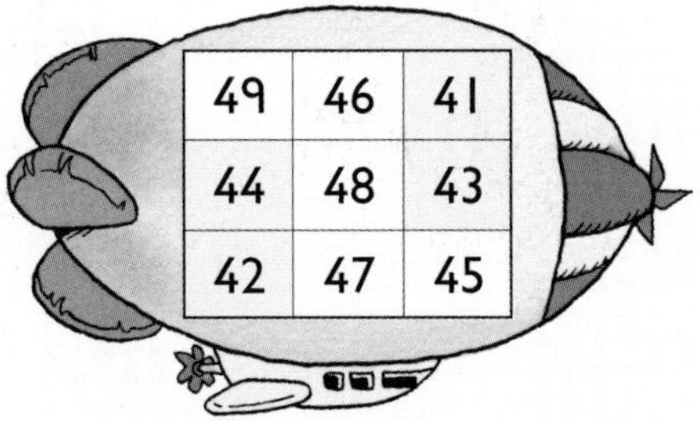

49	46	41
44	48	43
42	47	45

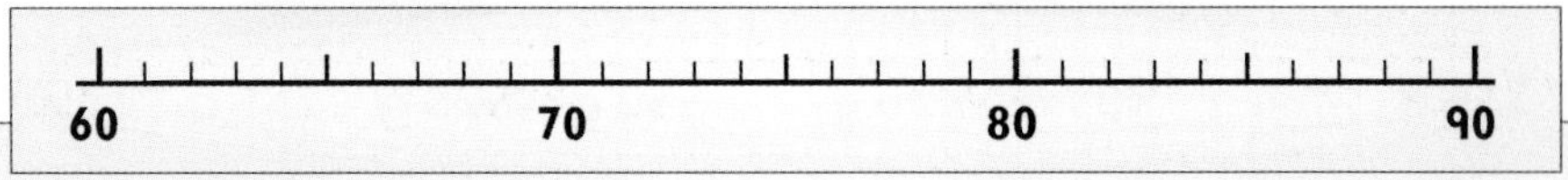

Write to the nearest ten.

72 →	70	77 →	80	64 →	60
86 →	90	68 →	70	83 →	80
59 →	60	91 →	90	52 →	50
27 →	30	34 →	30	65 →	70

21

Match.

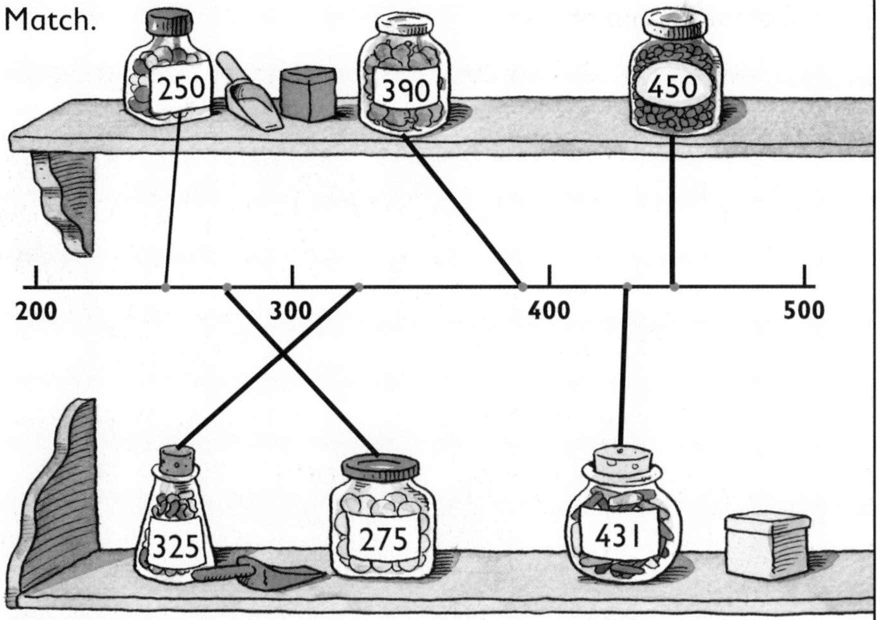

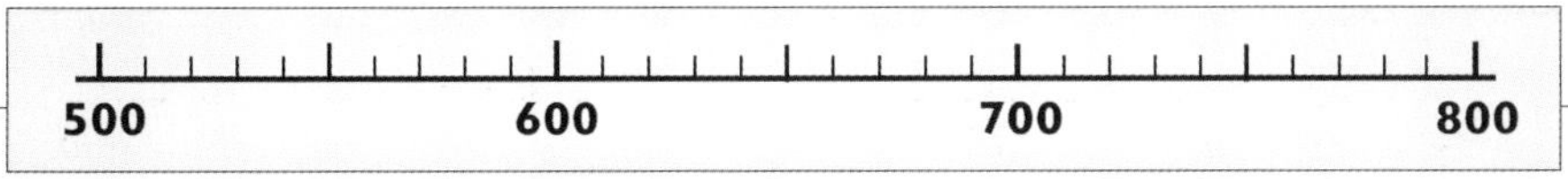

How many, to the nearest hundred?

520 →	500	690 →	700	740 →	700
575 →	600	721 →	700	686 →	700
493 →	500	817 →	800	234 →	200
555 →	600	947 →	900	750 →	800

22

Write each number.

Twenty.

20

Forty.

40

Seventy.

70

Eighty.

80

One hundred.

100

Three hundred.

300

Four hundred.

400

Six hundred.

600

Write in words.

Nine

Ninety

Two

Two hundred

Fifty

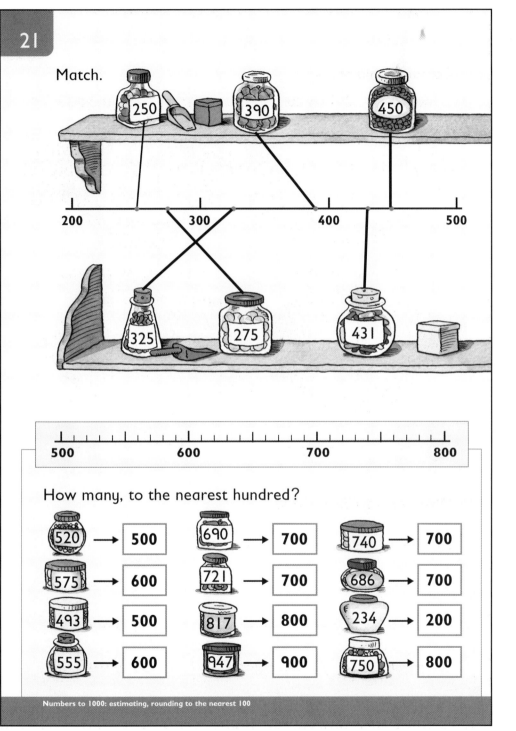

Five hundred

23

Colour to match.

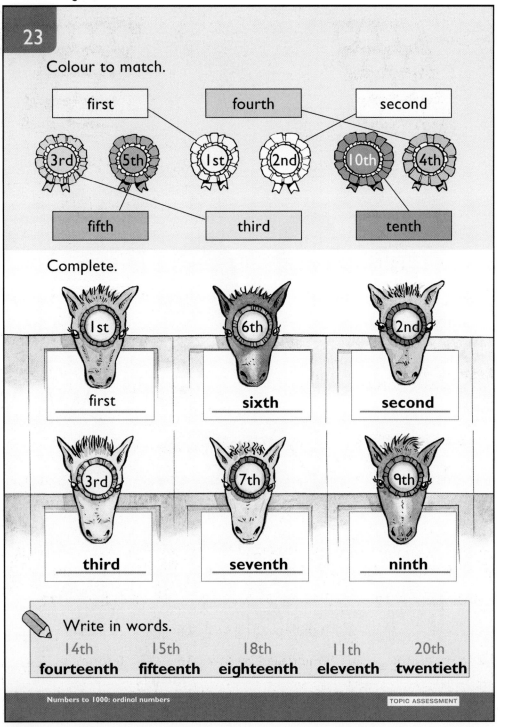

first | fourth | second

3rd | 5th | 1st | 2nd | 10th | 4th

fifth | third | tenth

Complete.

1st — first
6th — **sixth**
2nd — **second**
3rd — **third**
7th — **seventh**
9th — **ninth**

Write in words.

14th	15th	18th	11th	20th
fourteenth	**fifteenth**	**eighteenth**	**eleventh**	**twentieth**

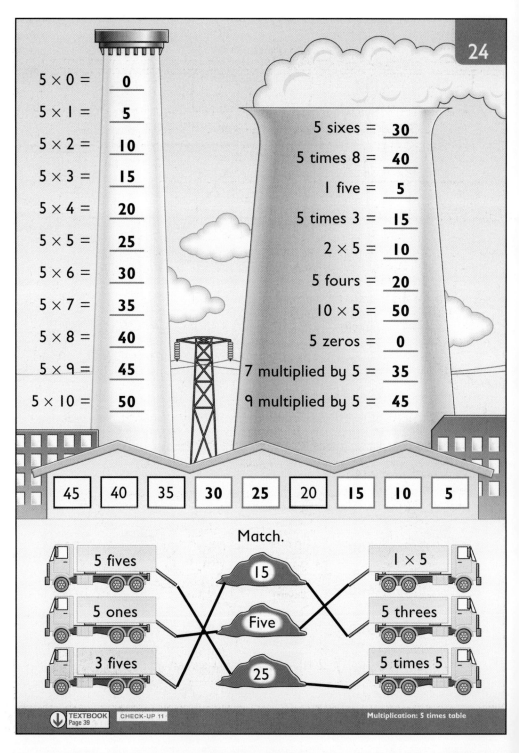

24

5 × 0 = **0**
5 × 1 = **5**
5 × 2 = **10**
5 × 3 = **15**
5 × 4 = **20**
5 × 5 = **25**
5 × 6 = **30**
5 × 7 = **35**
5 × 8 = **40**
5 × 9 = **45**
5 × 10 = **50**

5 sixes = **30**
5 times 8 = **40**
1 five = **5**
5 times 3 = **15**
2 × 5 = **10**
5 fours = **20**
10 × 5 = **50**
5 zeros = **0**
7 multiplied by 5 = **35**
9 multiplied by 5 = **45**

45 | 40 | 35 | **30** | **25** | 20 | **15** | **10** | **5**

Match.

5 fives | 15 | 1 × 5
5 ones | Five | 5 threes
3 fives | 25 | 5 times 5

25

$3 \times 0 =$ **0**	$3 \times 1 =$ **3**	$3 \times 2 =$ **6**
$3 \times 3 =$ **9**	$3 \times 4 =$ **12**	
$3 \times 5 =$ **15**	$3 \times 6 =$ **18**	
$3 \times 7 =$ **21**	$3 \times 8 =$ **24**	
$3 \times 9 =$ **27**	$3 \times 10 =$ **30**	

3 threes = **9**
3 times 4 = **12**
$7 \times 3 =$ **21**
0 threes = **0**
8 multiplied by 3 = **24**

3 tens = **30**
3 times 6 = **18**
$2 \times 3 =$ **6**
10 threes = **30**
1 multiplied by 3 = **3**

Colour to match.

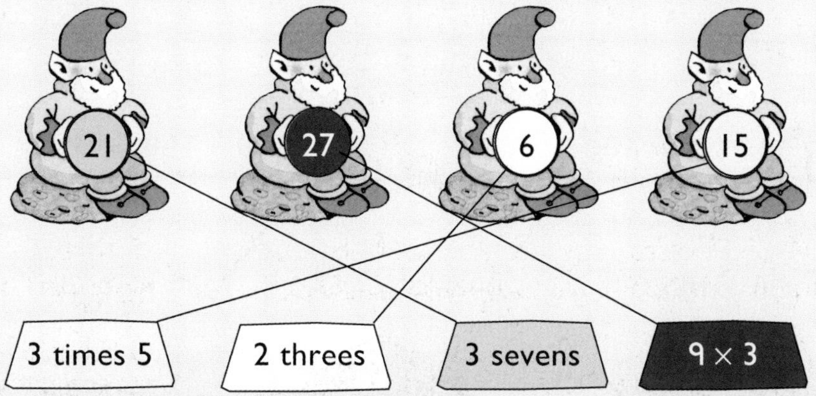

26

$4 \times 0 =$ **0**
$4 \times 1 =$ **4**
$4 \times 2 =$ **8**
$4 \times 3 =$ **12**
$4 \times 4 =$ **16**
$4 \times 5 =$ **20**

$4 \times 6 =$ **24**
$4 \times 7 =$ **28**
$4 \times 8 =$ **32**
$4 \times 9 =$ **36**
$4 \times 10 =$ **40**

Join in order.

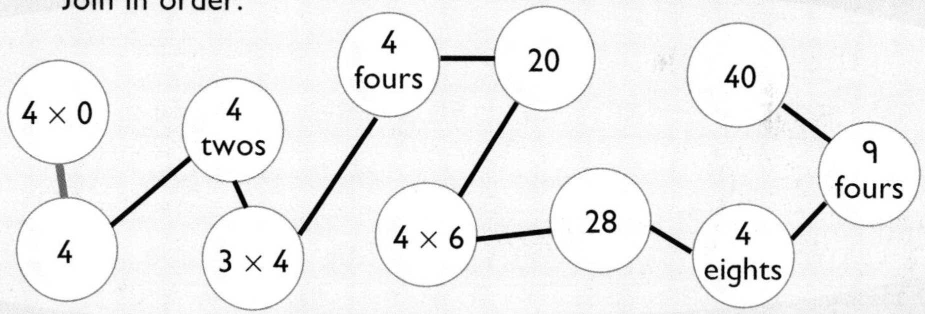

4 tens = **40**
4 threes = **12**
$7 \times 4 =$ **28**
2 fours = **8**

4 times 4 = **16**
4 times 0 = **0**
3 multiplied by 4 = **12**
9 multiplied by 4 = **36**

4 fives = **20**
4 eights = **32**
$1 \times 4 =$ **4**
6 fours = **24**

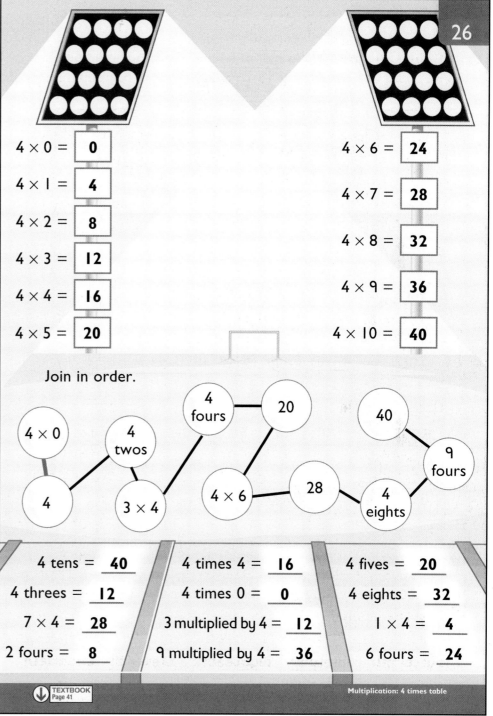

27

Colour multiples of 2 red.

1	2	3	4	5	6	7	8
9	10	11	12	13	14	15	16
17	18	19	20	21	22	23	24
25	26	27	28	29	30	31	32
33	34	35	36	37	38	39	40
41	42	43	44	45	46	47	48
49	50	51	52	53	54	55	56
57	58	59	60	61	62	63	64

Multiples of 2 end in

0 or **2** or **4** or **6** or **8**.

Colour multiples of 5 green.

1	2	3	4	5	6	7	8
9	10	11	12	13	14	15	16
17	18	19	20	21	22	23	24
25	26	27	28	29	30	31	32
33	34	35	36	37	38	39	40
41	42	43	44	45	46	47	48
49	50	51	52	53	54	55	56
57	58	59	60	61	62	63	64

Multiples of 5 end in

0 or **5**.

Complete each sequence of multiples.

10, 20, 30, **40**, **50**, **60**, **70**, **80**, **90**

900, 800, 700, **600**, **500**, **400**, **300**, **200**, **100**

50, 100, 150, **200**, **250**, **300**, **350**, **400**, **450**

Colour

blue	multiples of 2	98	49	202	447	55	190
red	multiples of 50	170	505	50	550	700	155
green	multiples of 100	500	550	300	700	805	1000

TEXTBOOK Page 44

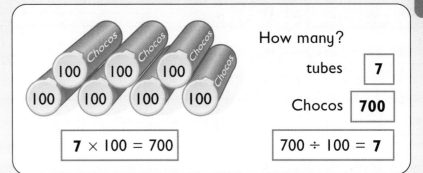

28

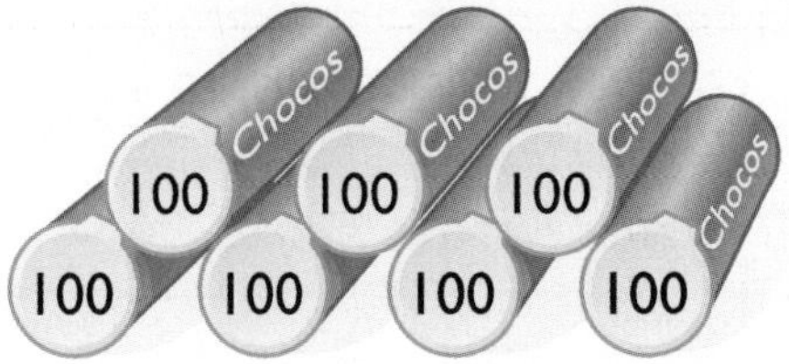

How many?

tubes **7**

Chocos **700**

7 × 100 = 700

700 ÷ 100 = **7**

How many?

packets **3**

Toffees **300**

3 × 100 = **300**

300 ÷ 100 = **3**

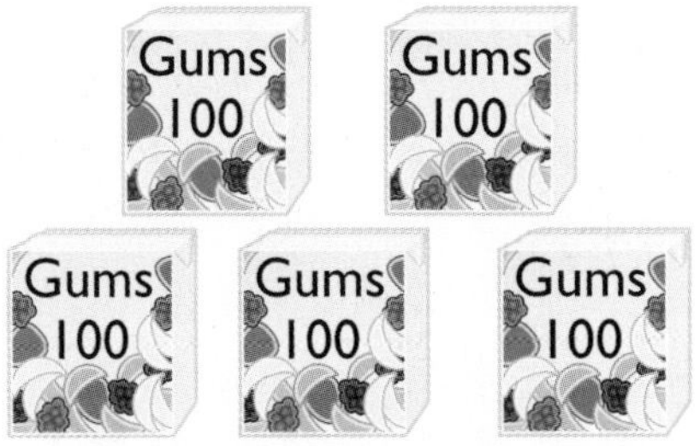

How many?

boxes **5**

Gums **500**

5 × **100** = **500**

500 ÷ **100** = **5**

800 ÷ 100 = **8**　　200 ÷ 100 = **2**　　1000 ÷ 100 = **10**

600 ÷ 100 = 6　　**400** ÷ 100 = 4　　**900** ÷ 100 = 9

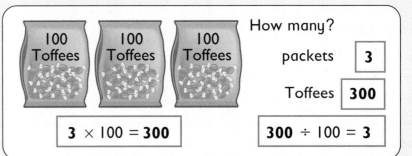

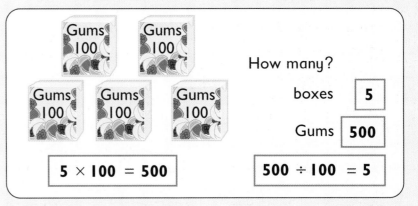

29

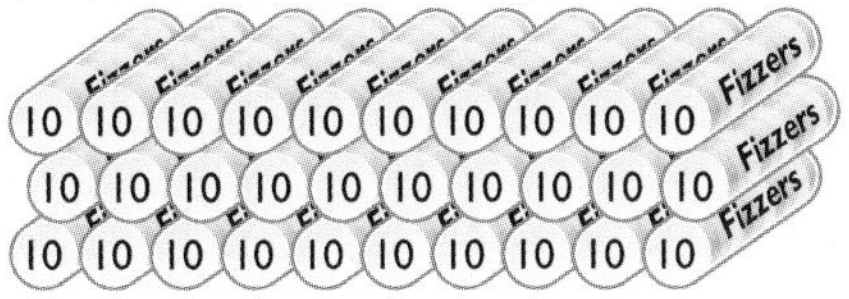

How many?

tubes **30**

Fizzers **300**

30 × 10 = 300

300 ÷ 10 = **30**

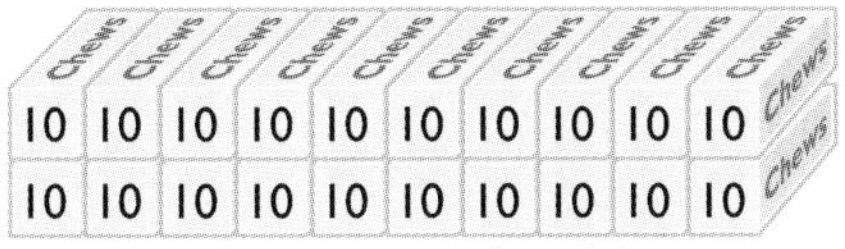

How many?

packets **20**

Chews **200**

20 × 10 = **200**

200 ÷ 10 = **20**

How many?

packs **40**

Gums **400**

40 × **10** = **400**

400 ÷ **10** = **40**

800 ÷ 10 = **80** 500 ÷ 10 = **50** 400 ÷ 10 = **40**

600 ÷ 10 = 60 **900** ÷ 10 = 90 **700** ÷ 10 = 70

300 ÷ 10 = **30**	1000 ÷ **100** = 10	**500** ÷ 10 = 50
300 ÷ 100 = **3**	1000 ÷ **10** = 100	**500** ÷ 100 = 5

30

Colour one tenth ($\frac{1}{10}$) of each shape.

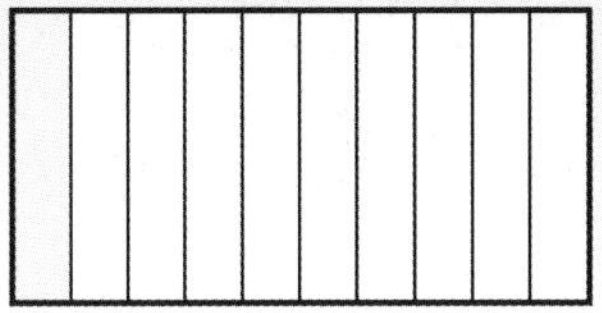

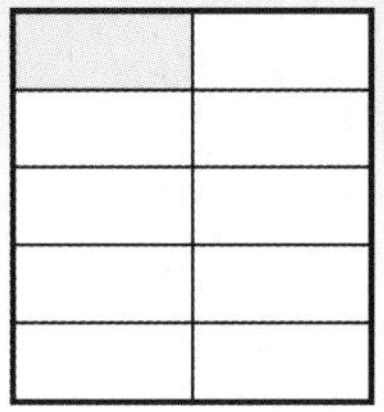

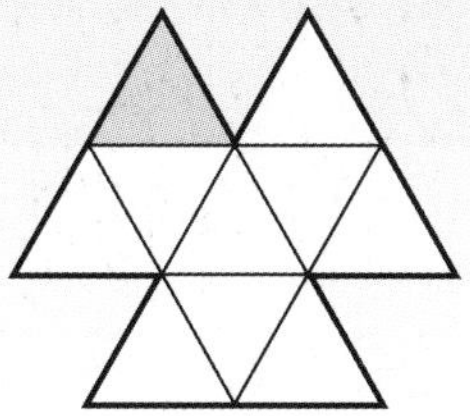

Tick (✓) the shapes which show tenths.

✓ 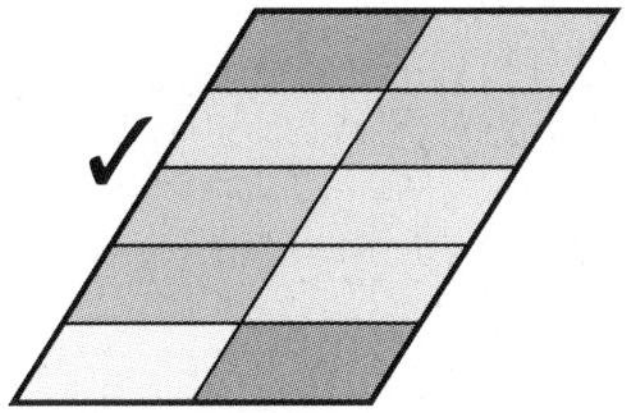

✓ 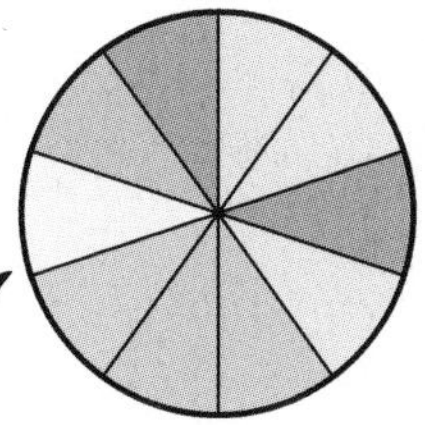

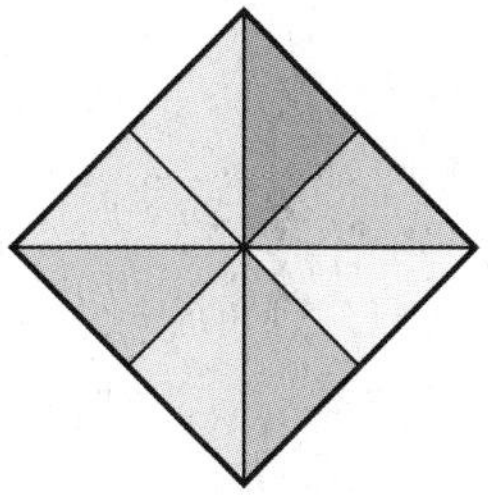

Colour

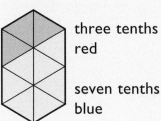

three tenths red

seven tenths blue

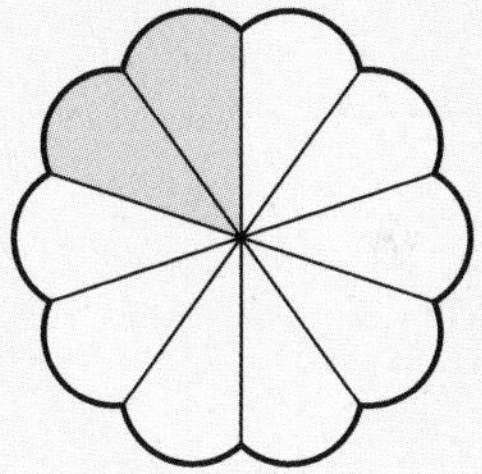

two tenths orange

eight tenths green.

What fraction of each shape is

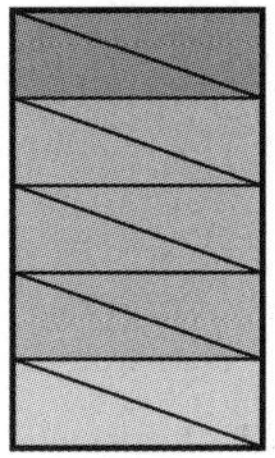

red $\frac{2}{10}$

blue $\frac{6}{10}$

green $\frac{2}{10}$

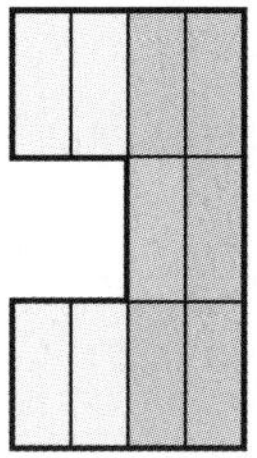

orange $\frac{5}{10}$

pink $\frac{1}{10}$

yellow? $\frac{4}{10}$

Nine tenths of a shape is red.
What fraction of the shape is **not** red? $\frac{1}{10}$

31

Colour one third ($\frac{1}{3}$) of each shape.

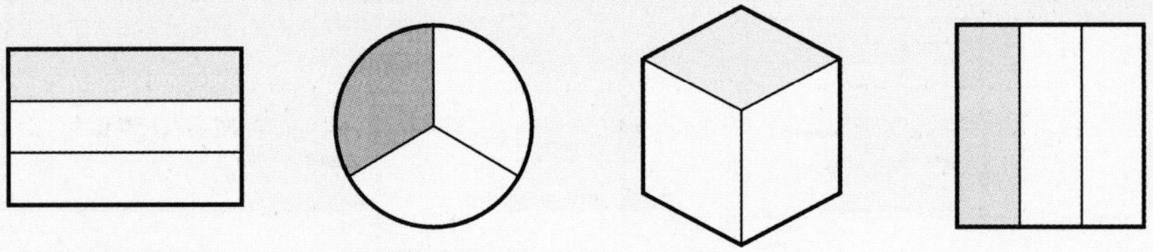

Tick (✓) the shapes which show thirds.

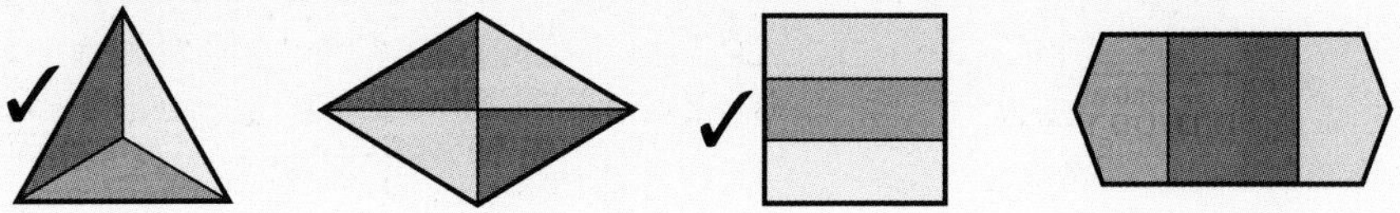

Colour

one third   two thirds   three thirds

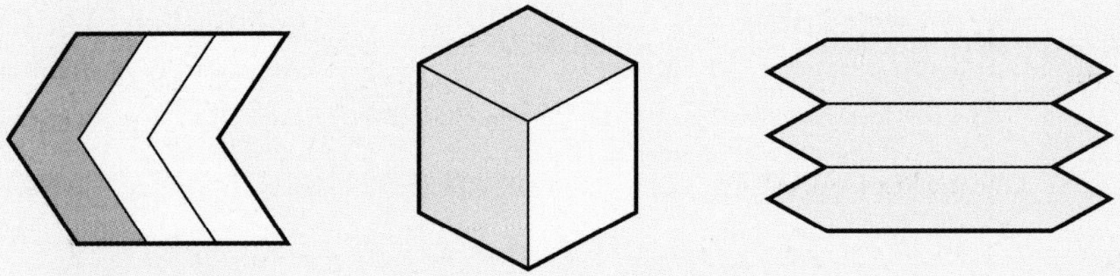

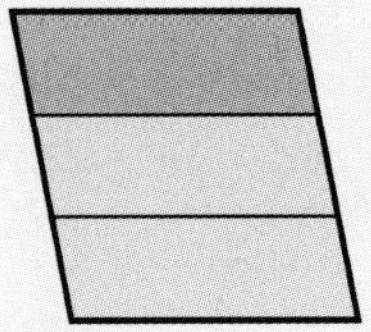

one third red
two thirds blue

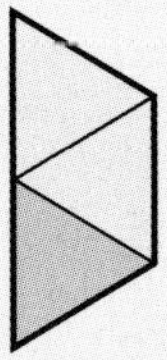

two thirds green
one third yellow.

What fraction of the rectangle is **not** red?

$\frac{2}{3}$

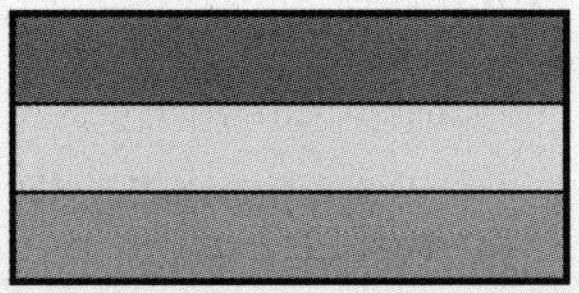

32

Colour one fifth ($\frac{1}{5}$) of each shape.

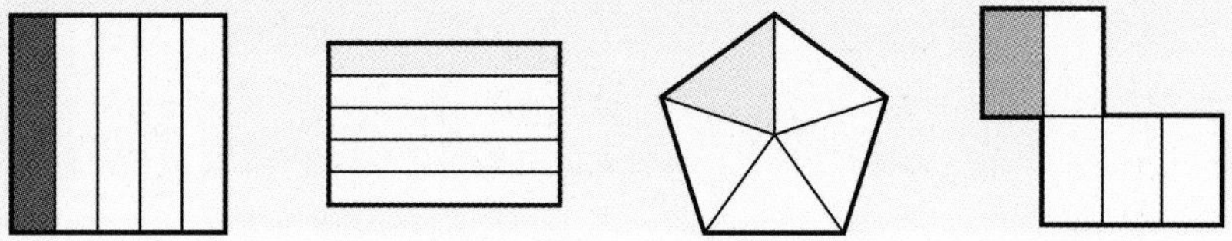

Tick (✓) the shapes which show fifths.

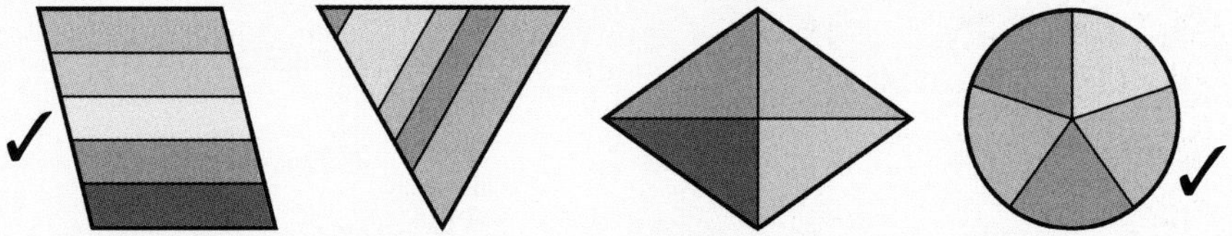

Colour

two fifths   four fifths   three fifths.

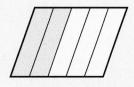

What fraction of each shape is

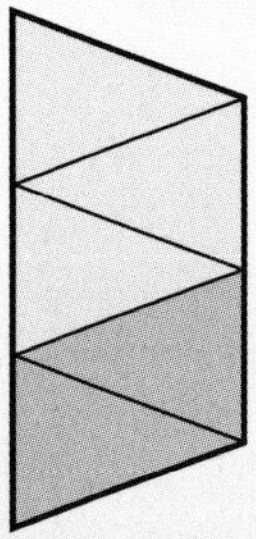

yellow $\frac{3}{5}$

green $\frac{2}{5}$

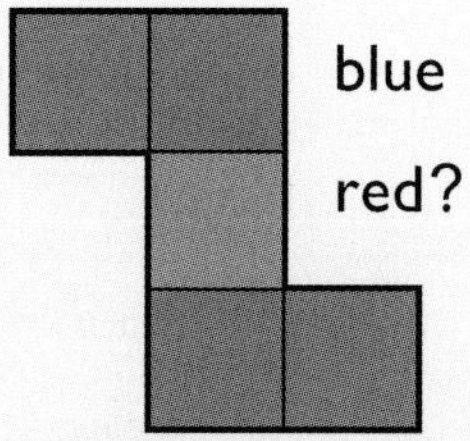

blue $\frac{1}{5}$

red? $\frac{4}{5}$

33

Complete the label on each bottle.

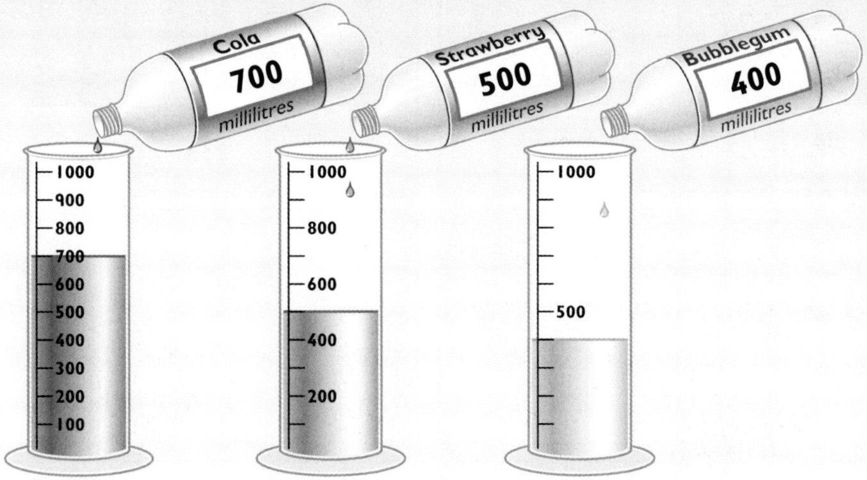

Which bottle contained ½ litre **Strawberry**

less than ½ litre **Bubblegum** more than ½ litre? **Cola**

Colour the jars to show the fruit juice.

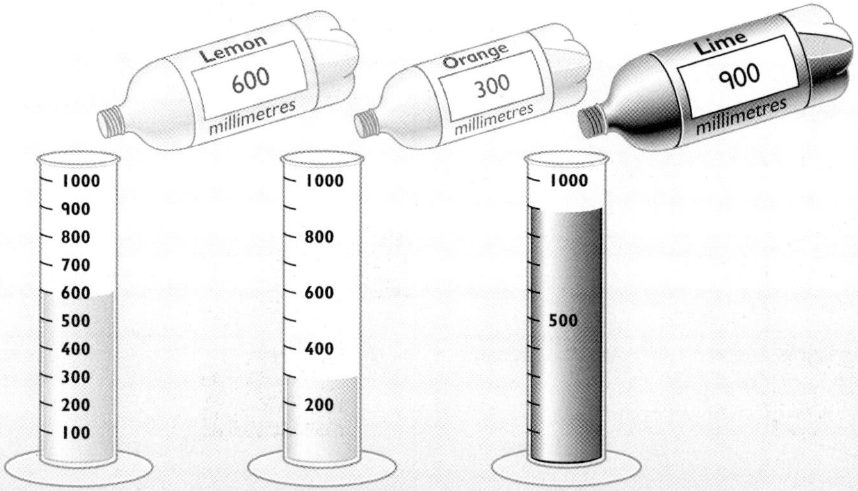

TEXTBOOK Page 96

34

Match.

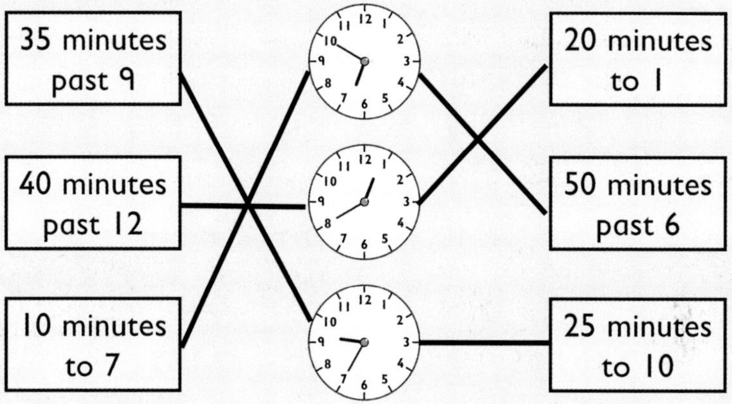

Write each time.

50 minutes past **2**

10 minutes to **3**

40 minutes past **7**

20 minutes to **8**

35 minutes past **5**

25 minutes to **6**

55 minutes past **2**

5 minutes to **3**

35

Write each time.

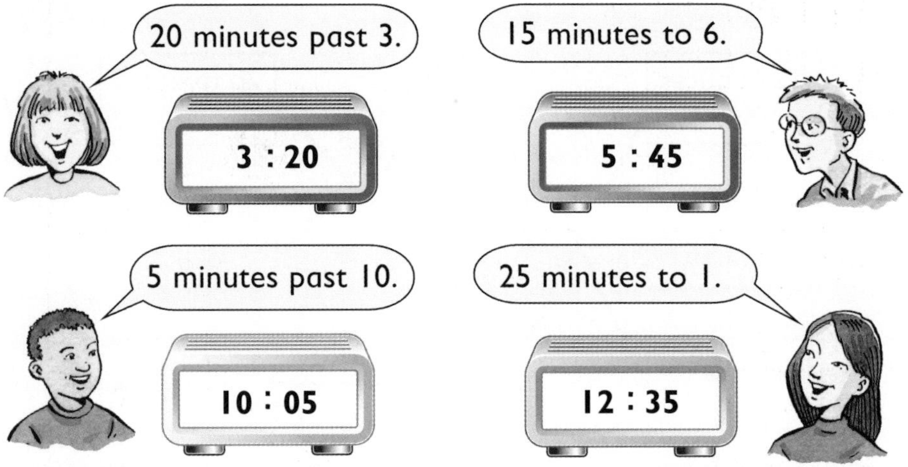

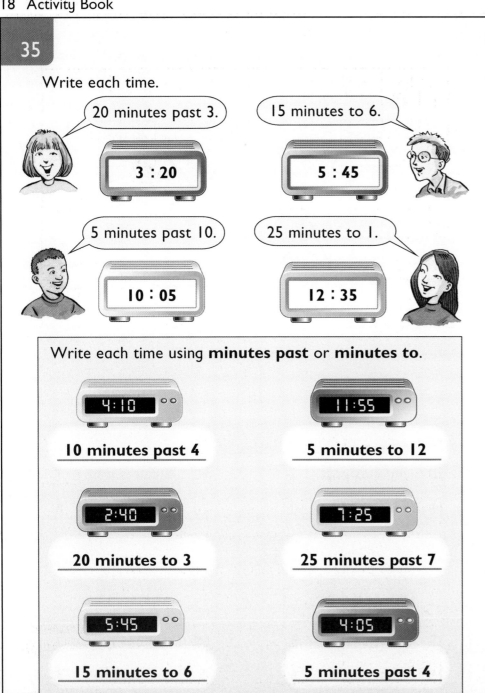

Write each time using **minutes past** or **minutes to**.

10 minutes past 4

5 minutes to 12

20 minutes to 3

25 minutes past 7

15 minutes to 6

5 minutes past 4

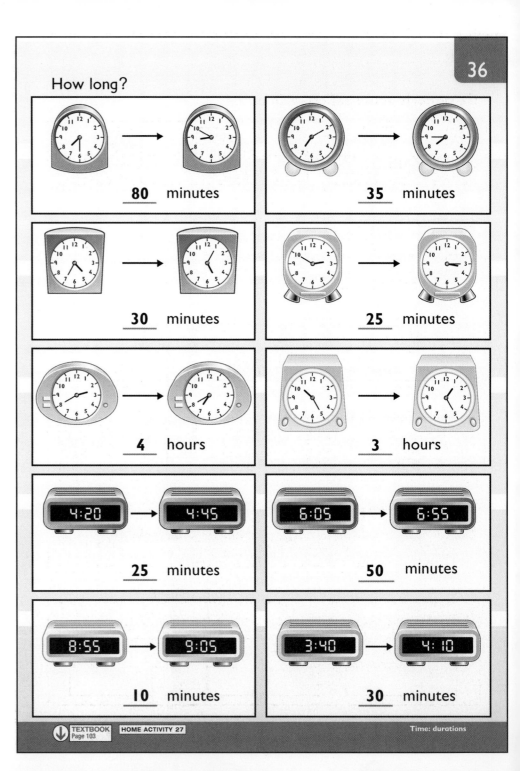

36

How long?

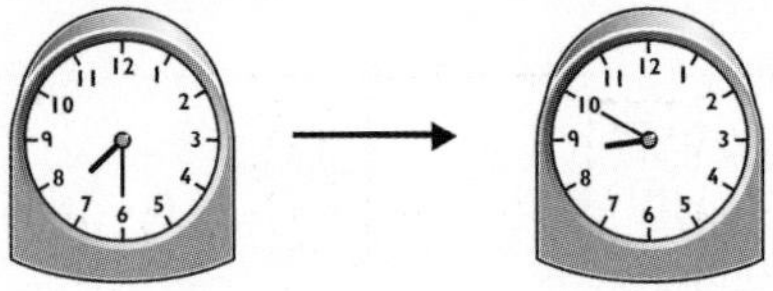

80 minutes

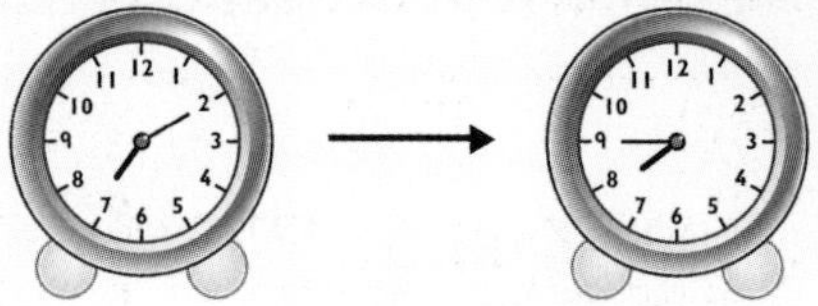

35 minutes

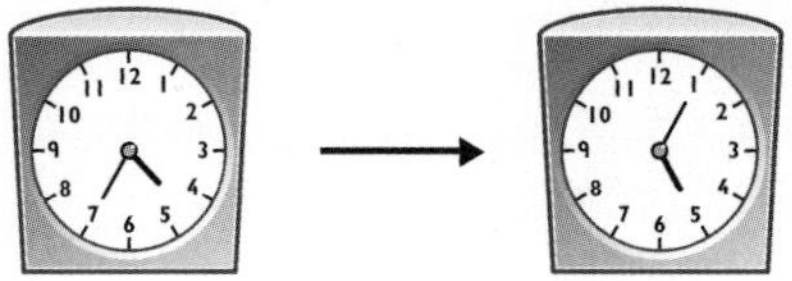

30 minutes

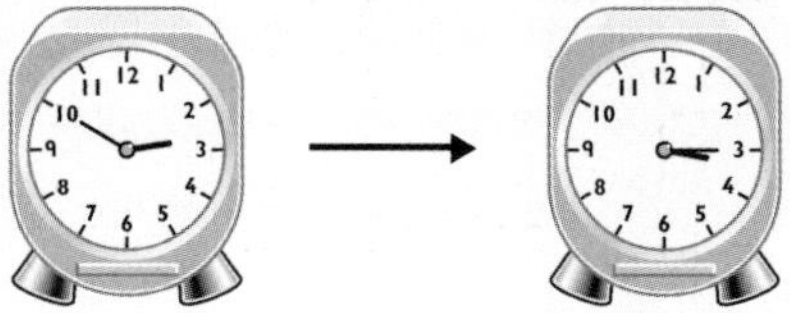

25 minutes

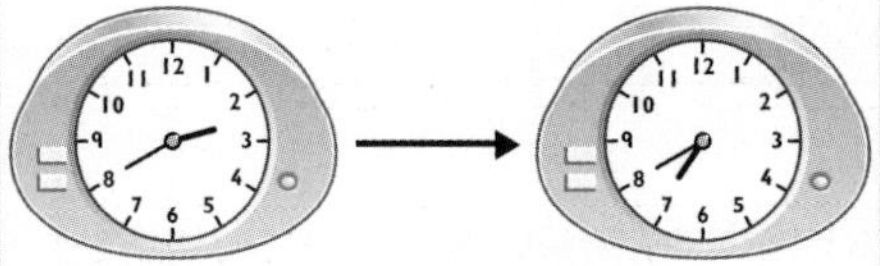

4 hours

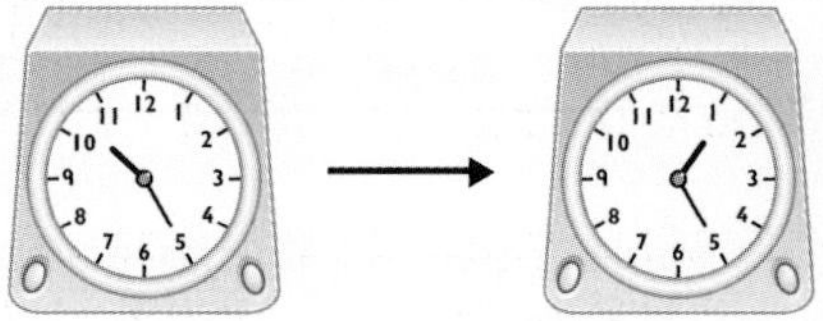

3 hours

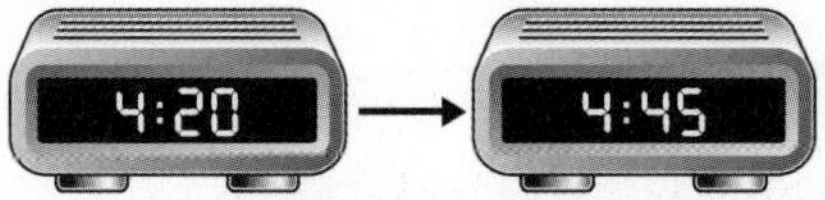

25 minutes

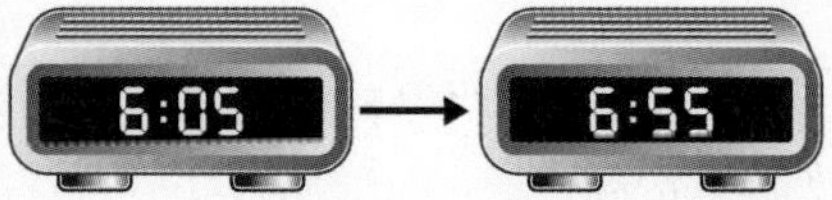

50 minutes

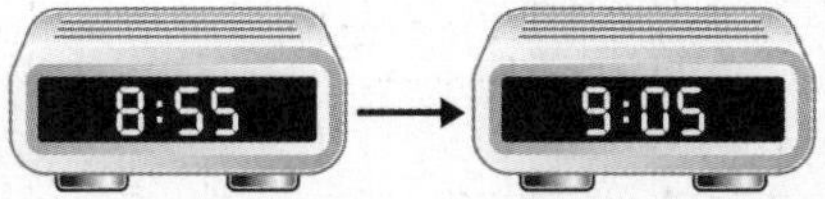

10 minutes

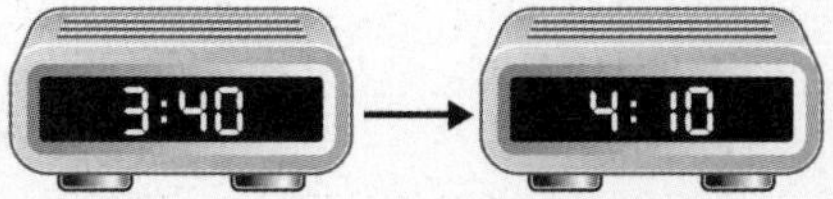

30 minutes

37

Draw each pattern. Colour it.

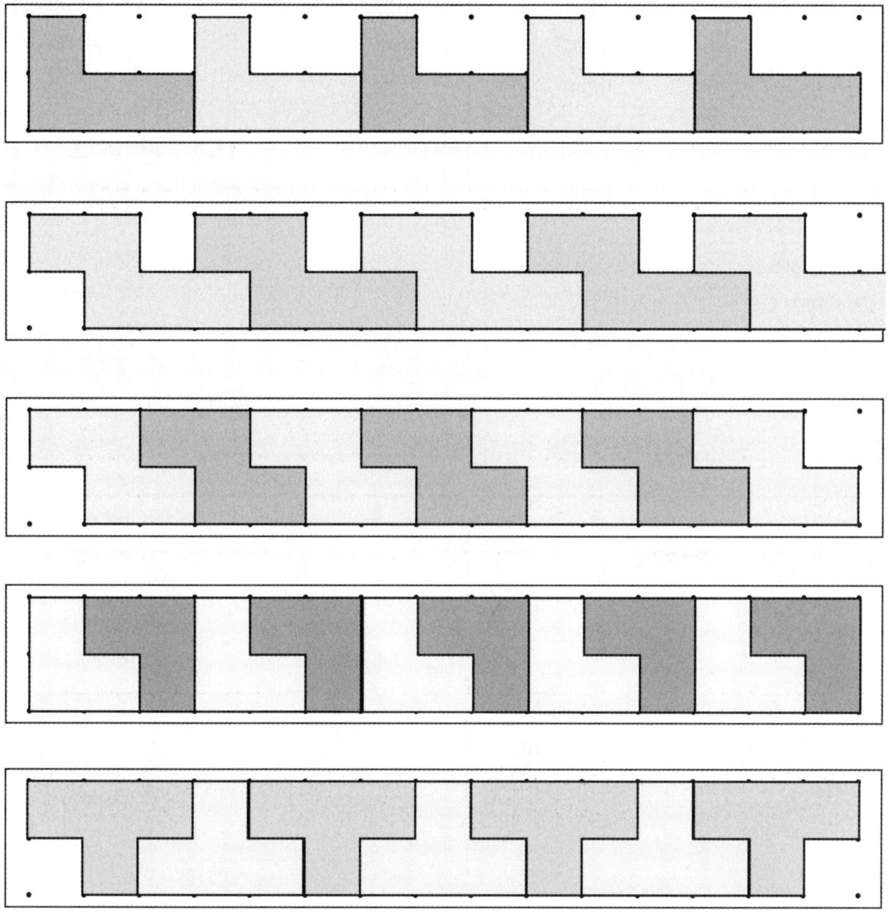

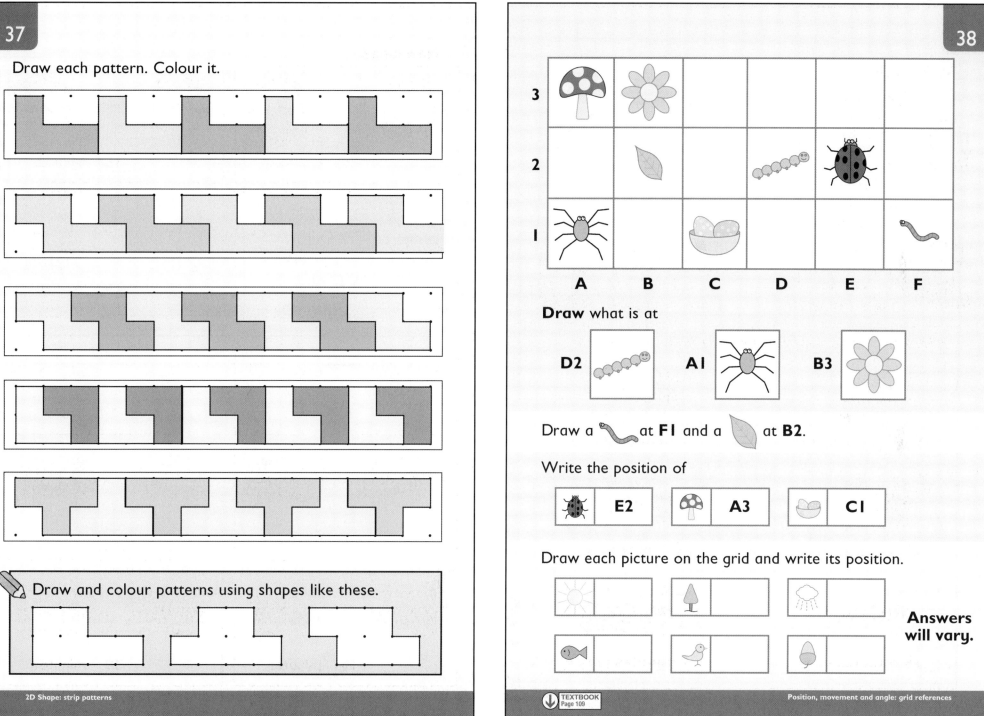

Draw and colour patterns using shapes like these.

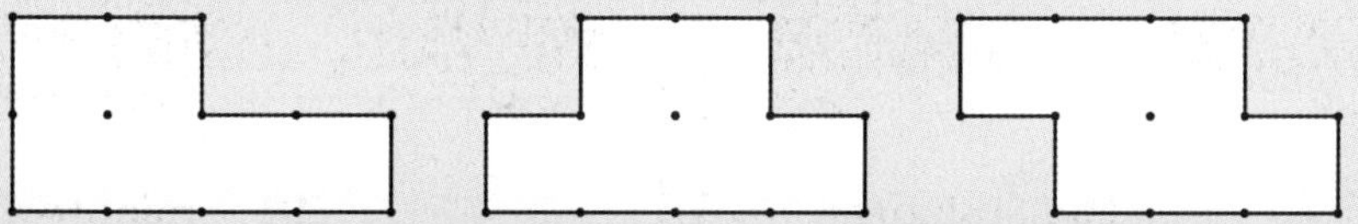

38

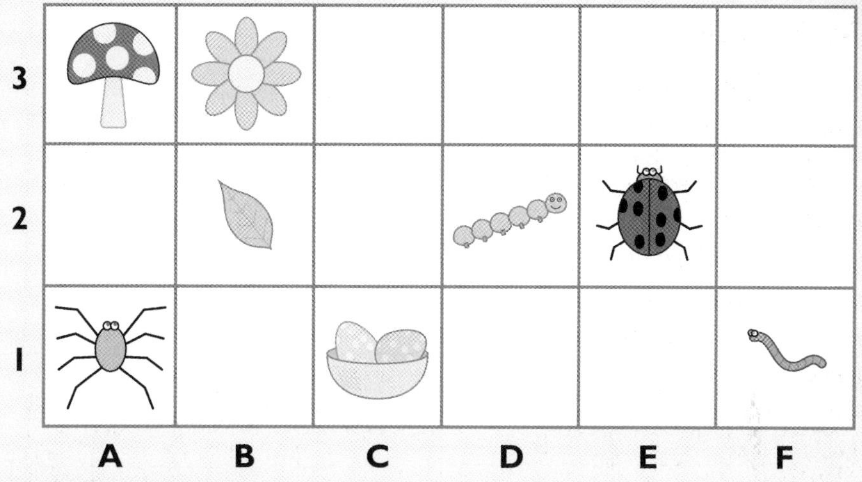

Draw what is at

D2  A1 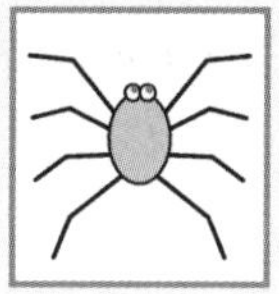 B3 

Draw a 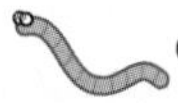 at **F1** and a  at **B2**.

Write the position of

	**E2**		**A3**		**C1**

Draw each picture on the grid and write its position.

Answers will vary.

39

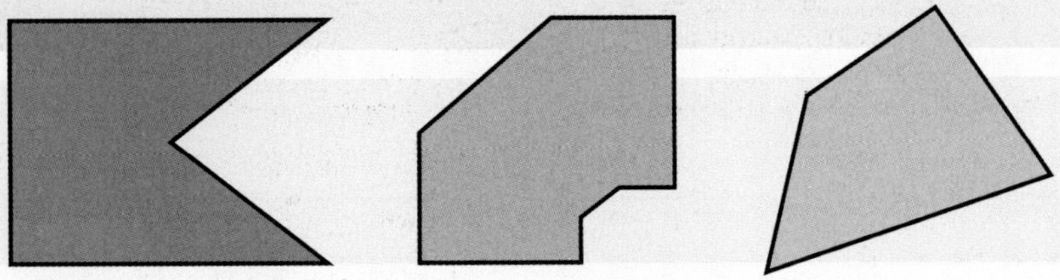

How many right angles are there in the

red shape **2** blue shape **4** green shape? **1**

Draw a shape with **only 3** right angles.

Draw a shape with **no** right angles.

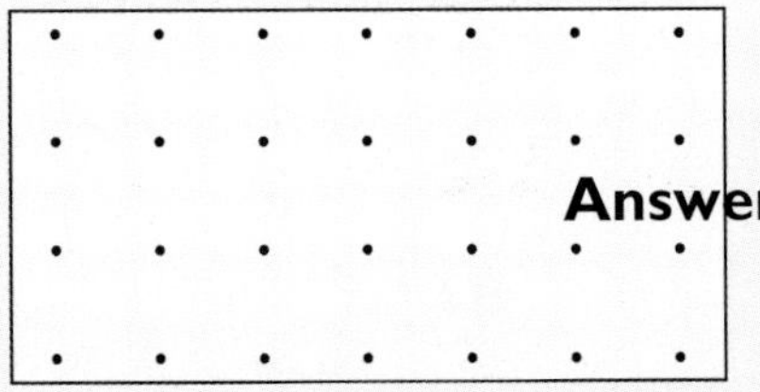

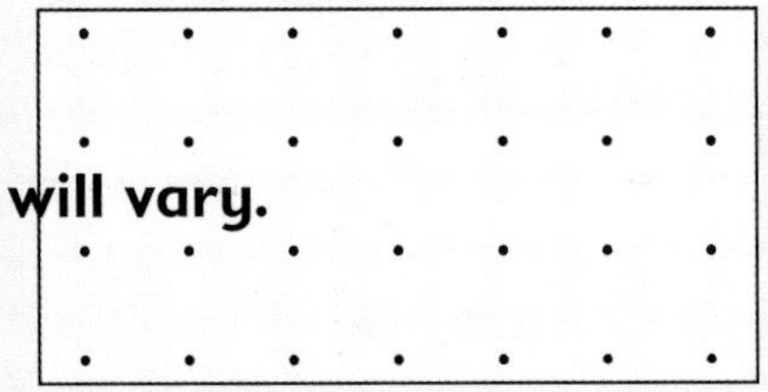

Answers will vary.

Colour blue, angles **larger** than a right angle.
Colour yellow, angles **smaller** than a right angle.

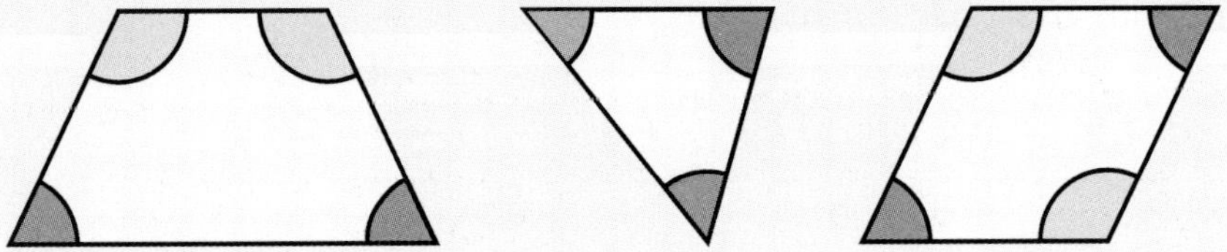

Tick (✓) the largest angle. Cross (✗) the smallest angle.

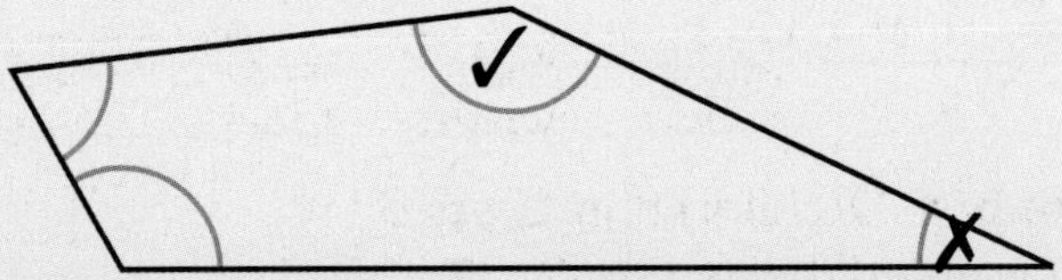

TEXTBOOK Page 110

40

Draw paths for these trips.
Write where each boat finishes.

F4, R, F1

Finishes at **Cove**

F3, R, F2, L, F1

Finishes at **Abbey**

F1, L, F2, R, F2

Finishes at **Bounty Bay**

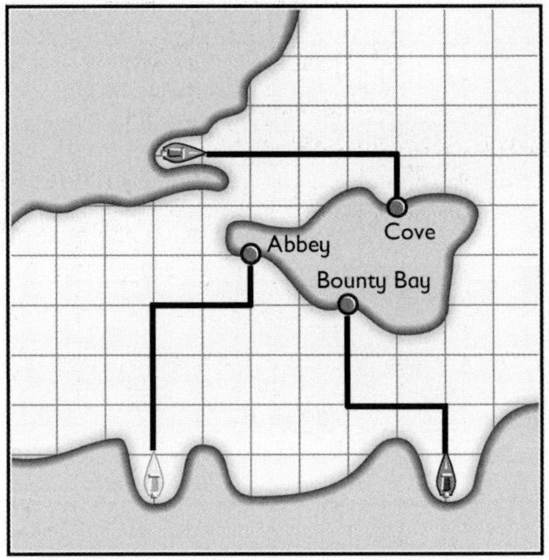

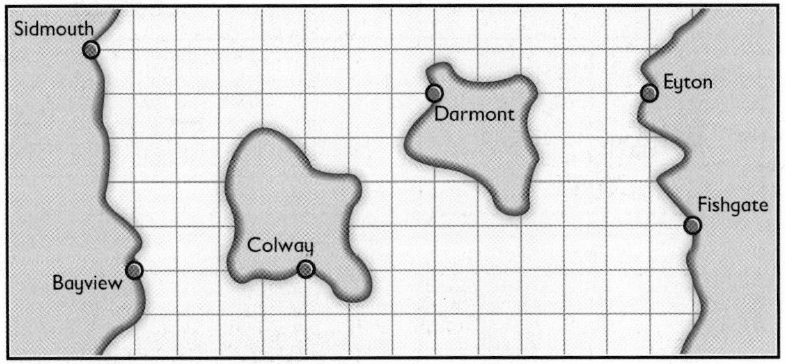

Draw, then write directions for a trip from

Bayview to Darmont **Answers will vary.**

Fishgate to Sidmouth

Eyton to Colway.

Colour to make each pattern symmetrical.

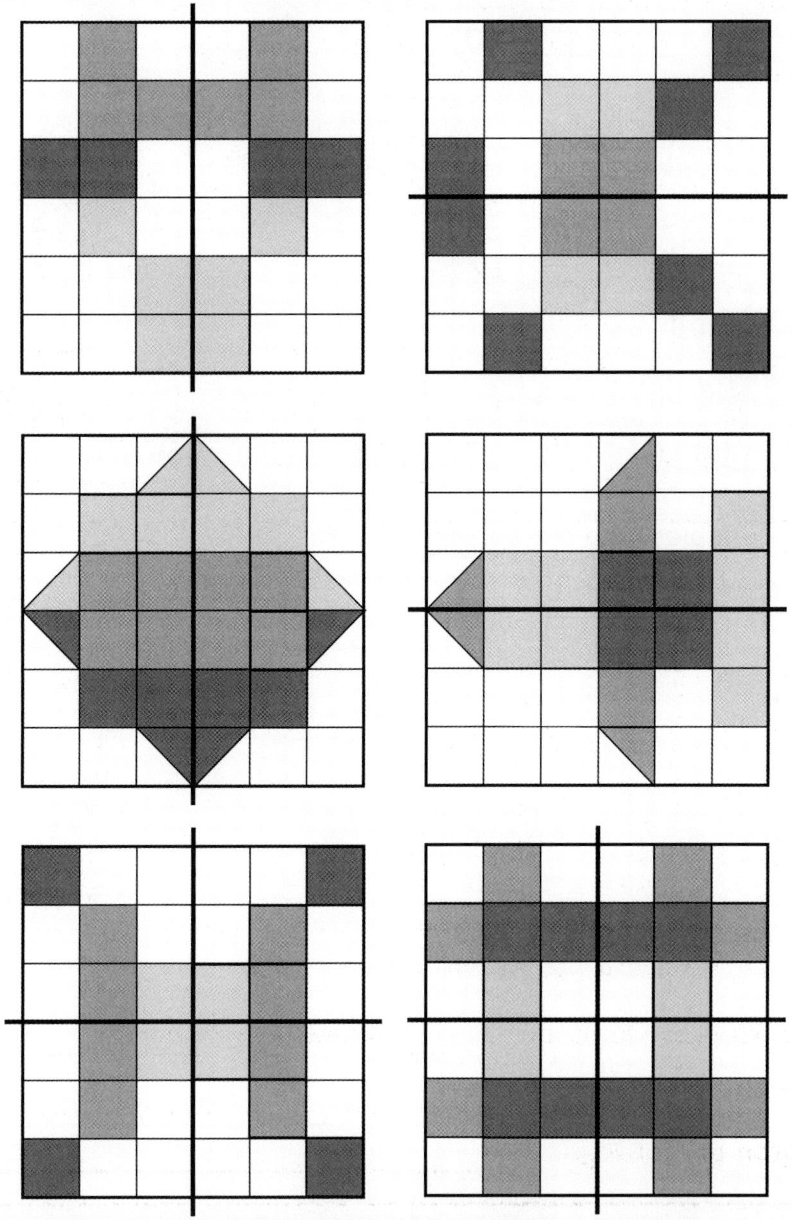

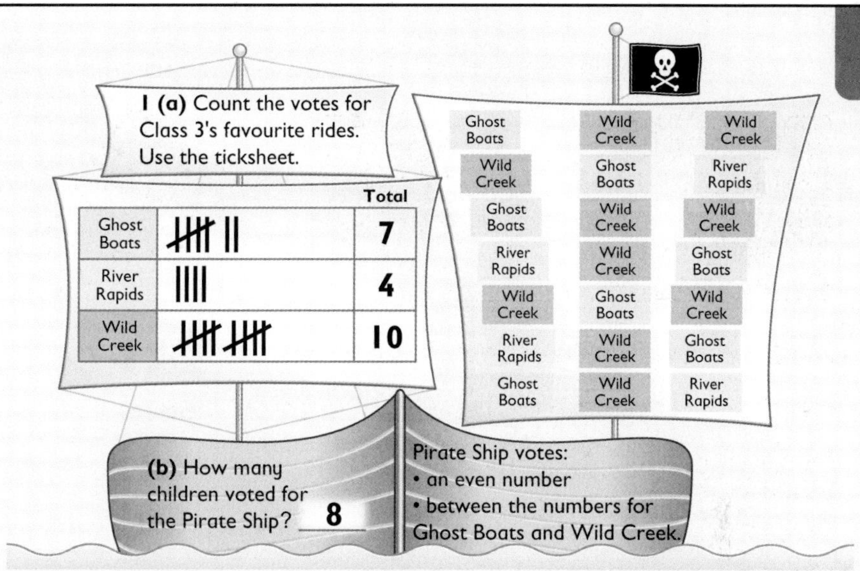

1 (a) Count the votes for Class 3's favourite rides. Use the ticksheet.

		Total
Ghost Boats	$\cancel{||||}$ ||	7
River Rapids	||||	4
Wild Creek	$\cancel{||||}$ $\cancel{||||}$	10

Ghost Boats	Wild Creek	Wild Creek
Wild Creek	Ghost Boats	River Rapids
Ghost Boats	Wild Creek	Wild Creek
River Rapids	Wild Creek	Ghost Boats
Wild Creek	Ghost Boats	Wild Creek
River Rapids	Wild Creek	Ghost Boats
Ghost Boats	Wild Creek	River Rapids

(b) How many children voted for the Pirate Ship? 8

Pirate Ship votes:
- an even number
- between the numbers for Ghost Boats and Wild Creek.

2 Complete the bar chart.

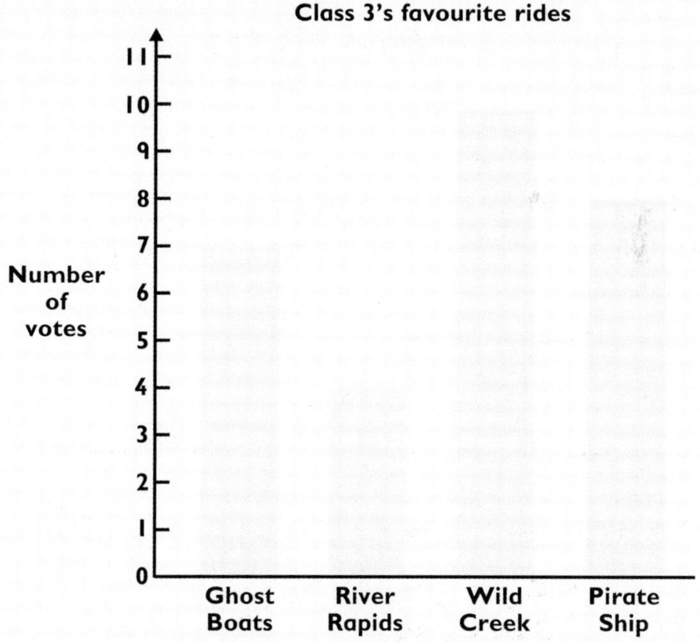

3 There are 32 children in Class 3.
How many did **not** vote? 3

43

1 Complete the table to show the number of children on each ride.

- The Swing Boat has 4 fewer children than the Roller Coaster.
- Altogether there are 39 children on these five rides.

Roller Coaster	13
Log Flume	6
Parachute	1
Swing Boat	9
Big Wheel	10

2 Complete the bar chart.

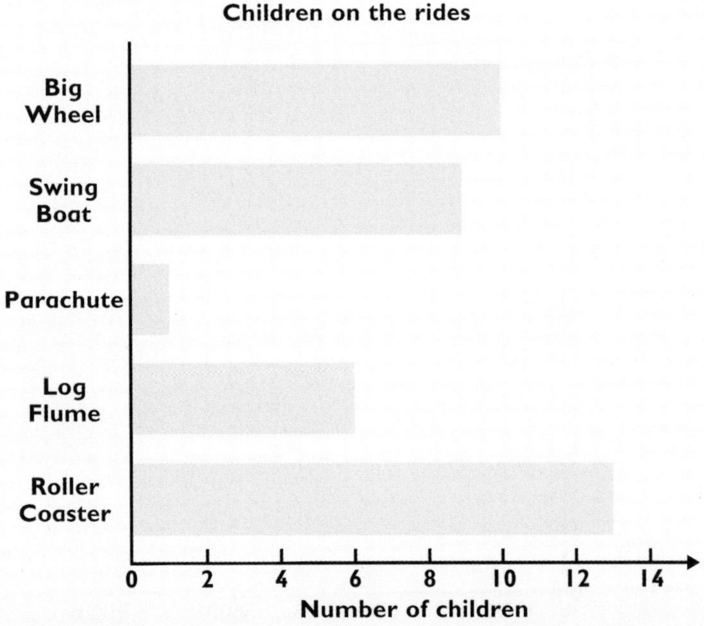

3 Draw a bar chart to show which rides the children in your class would **most** like to go on. **Children's answers will vary.**

TEXTBOOK Page 115

44

1 Class 3 bought these items in the Tuck Shop.

Count the items.
Use this tick sheet.

		Total
	卌 卌	10
	卌 II	7
	卌 IIII	9
	卌 I	6

2 Complete the pictogram.

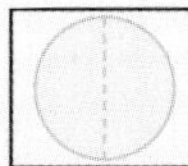 = 2 items

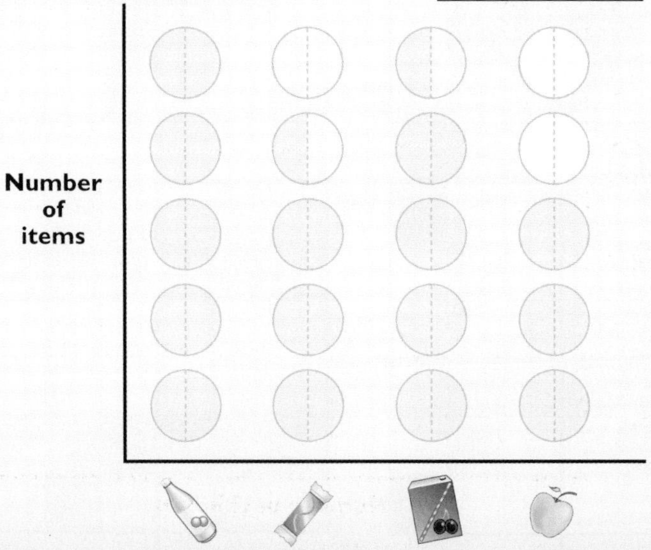

45

1 Find out how each child in your class comes to school.
Use this tick sheet.

Answers will vary.

		Total

Other		

2 Complete the pictogram.

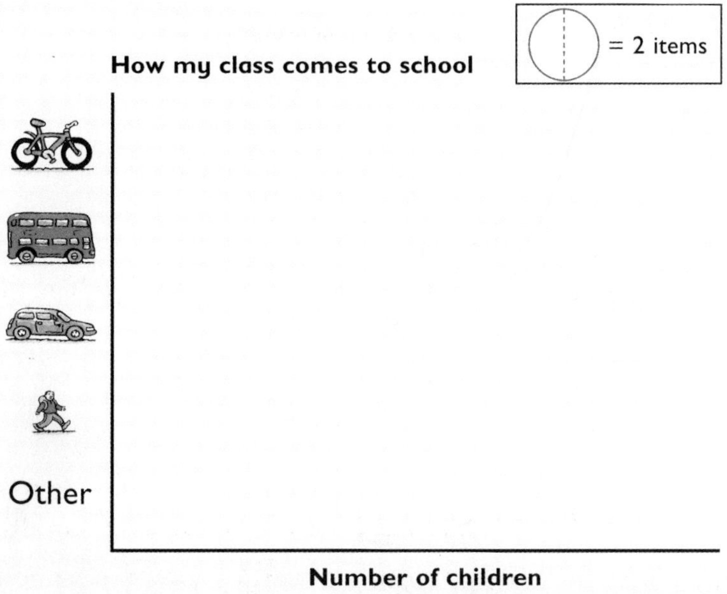

1

1 (a) 13 (b) 12 (c) 16 (d) 11
(e) 13 (f) 11 (g) 9 (h) 17

2 (a) 11 (b) 14 (c) 16

3 (a) 6 + 8 (b) 8 + 9 (c) 9 + 6

4 (a) 9 + **7** = 16 (b) 6 + **6** = 12 (c) Any two numbers adding to 12.
(d) **4** + 9 = 13 (e) ***10*** + 8 = 18 (f) Any two numbers adding to 11.

2

1 (a) 11 (b) 18 (c) 11 (d) 18
(e) 12 (f) 19 (g) 13 (h) 15

2 11 crabs

3 (a) 12 fish (b) 13 fish (c) 15 fish

4 14 fish

5 6 + 7 = 13
6 + 8 = 14
6 + 9 = 15, 7 + 8 = 15
7 + 9 = 16
8 + 9 = 17

3

1 (a) 12 (b) 19 (c) 15 (d) 20 (e) 17

2 (a) 15 (b) 19 (c) 17 (d) 14 (e) 16

3 (a) 18 (b) 17
(c) 16 (d) 19

4 (a) 16 (b) 19 (c) 19
(d) 18 (e) 18 (f) 14

5 (a) 15 + **4** = 19 (b) 1 + ***17*** = 18 (c) ***11*** + 2 = 13

4

1 (a) 19 (b) 18
(c) 17 (d) 16

2 (a) 17 (b) 14 (c) 19
(d) 18 (e) 15 (f) 18

3 (a) 12 + **3** = 15 (b) 19 + ***0*** = 19 (c) ***14*** + 3 = 17

4 (a) 15 + **5** (b) 9 + ***11*** (c) 17 + **3**
(d) **8** + 12 (e) 16 + **4** (f) ***10*** + 10
(g) 13 + **7** (h) **2** + 18 (i) ***14*** + 6

5

1 (a) 24 (b) 38 (c) 49 (d) 58
(e) 38 (f) 79 (g) 85 (h) 47
(i) 49 (j) 69 (k) 68 (l) 30

2 (a) 57p (b) 49p (c) 78p

3 98 bees

4 29 jars

5 (a) 30 + **8** = 38 (b) 84 + **3** = 87 (c) 9 + ***21*** = 30
(d) ***31*** + 5 = 36 (e) **5** + 72 = 77 (f) **93** + 6 = 99

6

1 (a) 42 (b) 57 (c) 39 (d) 61
(e) 78 (f) 85 (g) 70 (h) 93

2 (a) 70 (b) 90

3 10 + 90 = 100
20 + 80 = 100
30 + 70 = 100
40 + 60 = 100

4 (a) 75 (b) 79 (c) 93
(d) 88 (e) 95 (f) 91

5 (a) 24 + ***40*** = 64 (b) 46 + ***30*** = 76 (c) 20 + ***70*** = 90
(d) ***30*** + 15 = 45 (e) ***21*** + 70 = 91 (f) ***60*** + 19 = 79

7

1 (a) 39 (b) 56 (c) 68 (d) 84

2 (a) 37 (b) 64 (c) 71 (d) 95

3 (a) 69 (b) 75 (c) 87 (d) 93

4 (a) 41 (b) 54 (c) 78 (d) 92

5 (a) 54 (b) 56

6 (a) 62 (b) 64

7 (a) 91 (b) 68 (c) 85 (d) 99
(e) 85 (f) 56 (g) 97 (h) 90

8

1 (a) 58 (b) 49 (c) 76 (d) 98
(e) 48 (f) 89 (g) 67 (h) 37

2 Bob = 48 Fifi = 39 May = 60

3 (a) 26 + ***11*** = 37 (b) 42 + ***17*** = 59
(c) ***31*** + 18 = 49 (d) ***53*** + 13 = 66

9

1 (a) 58 (b) 89 (c) 88 (d) 58 (e) 86

2 (a) 78 (b) 98 (c) 79 (d) 95 (e) 60

3 (a) 68 litres (b) 50 litres
(c) 59 litres (d) 59 litres

4 (a) 31 litres (b) 29 litres

10

1 (a) 97p (b) 98p (c) 56p
(d) 94p (e) 78p (f) 90p

2 (a) tape and scraper
(b) scissors, tape and scraper

3 (a) 55 + ***45*** (b) ***95*** + 5
(c) 75 + ***25*** (d) 35 + ***65***
(e) ***55*** + 45 (f) ***15*** + 85

11

1 (a) 25p (b) 23p

2 (a) 21 (b) 22 (c) 24
(d) 24 (e) 28 (f) 22
(g) 21 (h) 21 (i) 25

3 (a) 84 (b) 42 (c) 63

4 (a) 92 (b) 52 (c) 31
(d) 61 (e) 74

5 (a) 3 (b) 28 (c) 8 (d) 97

12

1 82 passengers

2 (a) 52 (b) 62

3 (a) 91 (b) 91 (c) 81
(d) 45 (e) 66 (f) 72
(g) 36 + ***16*** = 52 (h) ***18*** + 27 = 45

4 Any from

45p + 15p = 60p	45p + 16p = 61p
45p + 17p = 62p	45p + 18p = 63p
56p + 15p = 71p	56p + 16p = 72p
56p + 17p = 73p	56p + 18p = 74p
68p + 15p = 83p	68p + 16p = 84p
68p + 17p = 85p	68p + 18p = 86p
77p + 15p = 92p	77p + 16p = 93p
77p + 17p = 94p	77p + 18p = 95p

13

1 (a) 72 (b) 94

2 Orange: 94 Purple: 81 Green: 92 Yellow: 100

3 (a) 91 (b) 61 (c) 73
(d) 91 (e) 82 (f) 76
(g) 67 + **24** = 91 (h) 25 + **47** = 72

14

1 (a) £22 (b) £25
(c) £30 (d) £21
(e) £30 (f) £39

2 (a) 37 (b) 32
(c) 36 (d) 26

3 (a) 17 + ***12*** + 3 = 32 (b) 7 + **4** + 11 = 22
(c) ***8*** + 13 + 13 = 34 (d) 19 + 5 + **5** + 10 = 39
(e) Any two numbers adding to 11.
(f) Any three numbers adding to 40.

4 Any five different numbers adding to 35.

15

1 (a) 9 + 11 5 + 15
4 + 16 7 + 13
(b) 15 + 2 + 3 15 + 4 + 1
11 + 7 + 2 10 + 7 + 3
13 + 3 + 4

(c) 1 + 2 + 8 + 9 1 + 3 + 7 + 9
1 + 4 + 6 + 9 1 + 4 + 7 + 8
1 + 5 + 6 + 8 2 + 3 + 6 + 9
2 + 3 + 7 + 8 2 + 4 + 5 + 9
2 + 4 + 6 + 8 2 + 5 + 6 + 7
3 + 4 + 5 + 8 3 + 4 + 6 + 7

2 **(a)** 41 **(b)** 43 **(c)** 84 **(d)** 16
(e) 29 **(f)** 26 **(g)** 55

3 **(a)** 79 **(b)** 50 **(c)** 95

16

1 **(a)** 14 **(b)** 40 **(c)** 49 **(d)** 23
(e) 65 **(f)** 17 **(g)** 15

2 **(a)** 95 **(b)** 95

17

1 **(a)** 5 **(e)** 9 **(i)** 8
(b) 9 **(f)** 5 **(j)** 9
(c) 7 **(g)** 8 **(k)** 6
(d) 7 **(h)** 9 **(l)** 5

2 **(a)** 8 **(b)** 6

3 **(a)** 4 **(b)** 7 **(c)** 7 **(d)** 4

4 **(a)** 14 – ***9*** = 5 **(b)** 12 – ***6*** = 6 **(c)** 11 – ***4*** = 7
(d) ***16*** – 8 = 8 **(e)** ***13*** – 5 = 8 **(f)** ***13*** – 4 = 9

18

1 **(a)** 20 **(b)** 14 **(c)** 1
(d) 10 **(e)** 6 **(f)** 12

2 **(a)** 18 **(b)** 13 **(c)** 19
(d) 15 **(e)** 9 **(f)** 7

3 **(a)** 17 fish **(b)** 9 fish

4 **(a)** 8 **(b)** 4
(c) 5 **(d)** 17
(e) 0 **(f)** 16

19

1 **(a)** 1 **(b)** 5 **(c)** 2
(d) 8 **(e)** 3 **(f)** 5
(g) 4 **(h)** 6 **(i)** 1

2 **(a)** 1 **(d)** 1
(b) 2 **(e)** 2
(c) 3 **(f)** 1

3 **(a)** 2 kg **(b)** 5 kg **(c)** 3 kg

4 **(a)** 19 – ***14*** = 5
(b) 17 – ***13*** = 4
(c) 15 – ***12*** = 3

20

1 **(a)** 3p **(b)** 1p **(c)** 3p
(d) 1p **(e)** 2p **(f)** 7p

2 **(a)** 2 **(c)** 4 **(e)** 4
(b) 2 **(d)** 4 **(f)** 1

3 **(a)** 4 **(b)** 1
(c) 6 **(d)** 3
(e) 6 **(f)** 2

4 **(a)** 18 – ***11*** = 7 **(b)** 17 – ***11*** = 6
(c) ***16*** – 14 = 2 **(d)** ***19*** – 10 = 9

21

1 **(a)** 7 – 2 = ***5*** **(b)** 9 – 6 = ***3*** **(c)** 8 – 5 = ***3***
17 – 2 = ***15*** 19 – 6 = ***13*** 18 – 5 = ***13***
27 – 2 = ***25*** 29 – 6 = ***23*** 28 – 5 = ***23***
57 – 2 = ***55*** 89 – 6 = ***83*** 78 – 5 = ***73***

2 **(a)** 61 **(b)** 32 **(c)** 90 **(d)** 22

3 **(a)** 53 **(b)** 74 **(c)** 32 **(d)** 45

4 **(a)** 64 grapes **(b)** 32 dates

5 **(a)** 43 **(b)** 54
(c) 91 **(d)** 61

6 **(a)** 47 – ***4*** = 43 **(b)** 68 – ***3*** = 65 **(c)** ***88*** – 6 = 82

22

1 **(a)** 37
(b) 48
(c) 54

2 **(a)** 35
(b) 9
(c) 41

3 **(a)** 2
(b) 56
(c) 43

4 **(a)** 72 – 60 = ***12***
(b) 84 – 40 = ***44***
(c) 83 – 70 = ***13***
(d) 57 – 30 = ***27***

5 **(a)** 69 – 40 = ***29***
(b) 43 – 20 = ***23***
(c) 99 – 80 = ***19***
(d) 60 – 30 = ***30***

6 **(a)** 56 – ***20*** = 36
(b) 71 – ***40*** = 31
(c) ***95*** – 30 = 65
(d) ***88*** – 60 = 28

23

1 **(a)** 27
(b) 53
(c) 74

2 **(a)** 28
(b) 52
(c) 36

3 **(a)** 17
(b) 56
(c) 85

4 **(a)** 59
(b) 14
(c) 33

5 **(a)** 38 **(b)** 15
(c) 26 **(d)** 12
(e) 21 **(f)** 21

6 **(a)** 64 **(b)** 35
(c) 17 **(d)** 49

7 33 soldiers

24

1 **(a)** 33 **(b)** 36 **(c)** 31

2 **(a)** 71 **(b)** 82 **(c)** 72
(d) 55 **(e)** 63 **(f)** 60

3 **(a)** 49 – 16 = ***33***
(b) 77 – 16 = ***61***
(c) 58 – 14 = ***44***
(d) 56 – 13 = ***43***

4 **(a)** 57 – ***12*** = 45
(b) 85 – ***14*** = 71
(c) ***67*** – 13 = 54
(d) ***36*** – 16 = 20

5 **(a)** 52 **(b)** 62

6 **(a)** 42 **(b)** 82
(c) 20 **(d)** 12

25

1 **(a)** 41 **(b)** 65 **(c)** 54
(d) 66 **(e)** 24 **(f)** 23

2 **(a)** 21 **(b)** 20 **(c)** 12
(d) 33 **(e)** 53 **(f)** 72

3 **(a)** 45 m **(b)** 12 m
(c) 22 m **(d)** 23 m

4 85 – 33 = 52 m

5 **(a)** 57 – ***25*** = 32 **(b)** 85 – ***44*** = 41 **(c)** 77 – ***23*** = 54

26

1 **(a)** 13 **(b)** 56

2 **(a)** 31 **(b)** 44

3 **(a)** 12 **(b)** 25

4 **(a)** 31 sailors **(b)** 25 sailors

27

1 **(a)** 18 **(b)** 16 **(c)** 18
(d) 16 **(e)** 19 **(f)** 16

2 **(a)** 18 **(b)** 17 **(c)** 16
(d) 17 **(e)** 15 **(f)** 19

3 **(a)** 23 – 8 = ***15*** **(b)** 21 – 4 = ***17*** **(c)** 22 – 9 = ***13***
(d) 23 – ***5*** = 18 **(e)** 24 – ***7*** = 17 **(f)** 24 – ***5*** = 19

4 apple, lemon

28

1 **(a)** 27 **(b)** 47
(c) 55 **(d)** 21 **(e)** 69

2 **(a)** 69 **(b)** 48 **(c)** 52
(d) 79 **(e)** 86 **(f)** 24

3 **(a)** 84 – 6 = ***78*** **(b)** 92 – 4 = ***88*** **(c)** 50 – 7 = ***43***
(d) 71 – ***2*** = 69 **(e)** 82 – ***4*** = 78 **(f)** 34 – ***5*** = 29

4 Lisa and Alex

29

1 **(a)** 19 **(b)** 27 **(c)** 8
(d) 29 **(e)** 38 **(f)** 12

2 **(a)** 69 **(b)** 46 **(c)** 36
(d) 58 **(e)** 47 **(f)** 79

3 **(a)** 58 **(b)** 67 **(c)** 56

4 **(a)** 21 – ***12*** = 9 **(b)** 41 – ***13*** = 28 **(c)** 62 – ***14*** = 48
(d) ***51*** – 13 = 38 **(e)** ***92*** – 15 = 77 **(f)** ***90*** – 16 = 74

30

1 **(a)** 17 **(b)** 16
(c) 29 **(d)** 18 **(e)** 45

2 **(a)** 38 **(b)** 28 **(c)** 39
(d) 28 **(e)** 49 **(f)** 46

3 **(a)** 16 more than Alan. 53 more than Babs.
(b) 37

4 **(a)** 75 – ***18*** = 57 **(b)** 67 – ***28*** = 39 **(c)** 94 – ***38*** = 56
(d) ***82*** – 47 = 35 **(e)** ***94*** – 37 = 57 **(f)** ***72*** – 36 = 36

31

1 **(a)** 46 **(b)** 23 **(c)** 68

2 **(a)** 45 **(b)** 22

3 **(a)** 21 **(b)** 43 **(c)** 43
(d) 13 **(e)** 30 **(f)** 35
(g) 31 **(h)** 65 **(i)** 32

4 51

5 **(a)** 84 **(b)** 61
(c) 34 **(d)** 52

32

1 **(a)** 14 **(b)** 16 **(c)** 37 **(d)** 28

2 **(a)** 28 **(b)** 49 **(c)** 28
(d) 38 **(e)** 38 **(f)** 63
(g) 45 **(h)** 28

3 **(a)** 26p **(b)** 67p **(c)** 15p **(d)** 38p

33

1 **(a)** 9 + 8 = 17
8 + 9 = ***17***
17 – 9 = ***8***
17 – 8 = ***9***

(b) 12 + 24 = ***36***
24 + 12 = ***36***
36 – 12 = ***24***
36 – 24 = ***12***

(c) 59 – 24 = ***35***
59 – 35 = ***24***
24 + 35 = ***59***
35 + 24 = ***59***

(d) 88 – 35 = ***53***
88 – 53 = ***35***
35 + 53 = ***88***
53 + 35 = ***88***

2 **(a)** 18 – 11 = 7 18 – 7 = 11
(b) 37 – 23 = 14 37 – 14 = 23
(c) 65 – 42 = 23 65 – 23 = 42
(d) 99 – 65 = 34 99 – 34 = 65

34

1 **(a)** 7 + 6 = ***13***
6 + 7 = ***13***
13 – 6 = ***7***
13 – 7 = ***6***

(b) 8 + 14 = ***22***
14 + 8 = ***22***
22 – ***8*** = ***14***
22 – 14 = ***8***

2 **(a)** 6 + 9 = 15
9 + 6 = 15
15 – 6 = 9
15 – 9 = 6

(b) 12 + 9 = 21
9 + 12 = 21
21 – 12 = 9
21 – 9 = 12

(c) 8 + 19 = 27
19 + 8 = 27
27 – 8 = 19
27 – 19 = 8

(d) 5 + 28 = 33
28 + 5 = 33
33 – 5 = 28
33 – 28 = 5

3 **(a)** 11 + 14 = 25 or 12 + 13 = 25
14 + 11 = 25 13 + 12 = 25
25 – 11 = 14 25 – 12 = 13
25 – 14 = 11 25 – 13 = 12

(b) 15 + 23 = 38 or 18 + 20 = 38
23 + 15 = 38 20 + 18 = 38
38 – 15 = 23 38 – 18 = 20
38 – 23 = 15 38 – 20 = 18

(c) 24 + 26 = 50 or 18 + 32 = 50
26 + 24 = 50 32 + 18 = 50
50 – 24 = 26 50 – 18 = 32
50 – 26 = 24 50 – 32 = 18

35

1 **(a)** 12 **(b)** 64
(c) 52 **(d)** 52
(e) 24 **(f)** 26

2 **(a)** even number
(b) odd number
(c) odd number – odd number = even number

3 **(a)** 72, 83 and 94
(b) Marco drives 83 Chic drives 72 Ena drives 94

36

1 Alan's cost 41p. He has 39p left.
Beth's cost 15p. She has 53p left.
Carlo's cost 45p. He has 30p left.
Don's cost 79p. He has 17p left.
Eric's cost 72p. He has 19p left.
Fay's cost 81p. She has 19p left.

2 **(a)** 27p
(b) Amy bought blue and green.
Ron bought blue, orange and yellow.

37

1 **(a)** 10p **(b)** 16p **(c)** 20p

2 **(a)** 6 **(b)** 0 **(c)** 14 **(d)** 8
(e) 18 **(f)** 2 **(g)** 4 **(h)** 12
(i) 2 × ***7*** = 14 **(j)** 2 × ***10*** = 20 **(k)** 2 × ***4*** = 8

3 **(a)** 12 **(b)** 19 **(c)** 19 **(d)** 22

38

1 **(a)** 50 **(b)** 80 **(c)** 100 **(d)** 70

2 **(a)** 40 **(b)** 90 **(c)** 0 **(d)** 60
(e) 20 **(f)** 100 **(g)** 30 **(h)** 10
(i) 10 × **7** = 70 **(j)** 10 × **5** = 50 **(k)** 10 × **9** = 90

3 **(a)** 20 **(b)** 60 **(c)** 80 **(d)** 30 **(e)** 10 **(f)** 40

39

1 **(a)** 35 **(b)** 10 **(c)** 50
(d) 15 **(e)** 30 **(f)** 40
(g) 32 **(h)** 30

2 **(a)** 45 **(b)** 25 **(c)** 35

3 **(a)** 15 helmets
(b) 40 helmets
(c) 30 helmets
(d) 20 helmets

4 **(a)** 5 × ***1*** = 5 **(b)** 5 × ***0*** = 0 **(c)** 5 × **2** = 10
(d) ***9*** × 5 = 45 **(e)** ***3*** × 5 = 15 **(f)** ***10*** × 5 = 50

40

1 **(a)** 18 **(b)** 21
(c) 12 **(d)** 30

2 **(a)** 15 litres **(b)** 30 litres **(c)** 24 litres **(d)** 27 litres

3 **(a)** Ali has more.
(b) 1 litre more
(c) 60 litres

4 **(a)** 3 × ***0*** = 0 **(b)** 3 × **4** = 12 **(c)** 3 × **2** = 6
(d) ***1*** × 3 = 3 **(e)** ***3*** × 3 = 9 **(f)** ***8*** × 3 = 24
(g) 3 × **5** = 15 **(h)** ***9*** × 3 = 27 **(i)** 3 × **6** = 18

41

1 **(a)** £28 **(b)** £12 **(c)** £40

2 **(a)** £32 **(b)** £36 **(c)** £32 **(d)** £24
(e) £36 **(f)** £25

3 **(a)** 4 × ***6*** = 24 **(b)** 4 × ***0*** = 0 **(c)** 4 × ***1*** = 4
(d) ***5*** × 4 = 20 **(e)** ***9*** × 4 = 36 **(f)** ***10*** × 4 = 40

42

1 **(a)** 18 **(b)** 24 **(c)** 30

2 **(a)** 12 **(b)** 21 **(c)** 27

3 **(a)** 24 **(b)** 32 **(c)** 40

4 **(a)** 20 **(b)** 16 **(c)** 0
(d) 9 **(e)** 28 **(f)** 8
(g) 45 **(h)** 30 **(i)** 15

5 **(a)** 5 × **2** = 10 **(b)** 7 × **5** = 35 **(c)** 4 × ***9*** = 36
(d) ***10*** × 5 = 50 **(e)** ***3*** × 4 = 12 **(f)** ***5*** × 3 = 15

43

1 **(a)** 16 dollars **(b)** 50 dollars **(c)** 12 dollars
(d) 24 dollars **(e)** 40 dollars **(f)** 40 dollars
(g) 100 dollars **(h)** 18 dollars **(i)** 18 dollars

2 **(a)** 45 **(b)** 8 **(c)** 0
(d) 80 **(e)** 15 **(f)** 70

3 **(a)** 16 **(b)** 32

4 **(a)** 30 **(b)** 60

5 **(a)** 2 × ***7*** = 14 **(b)** 3 × ***10*** = 30 **(c)** 10 × **4** = 40
(d) ***5*** × 5 = 25 **(e)** ***6*** × 2 = 12 **(f)** ***0*** × 10 = 0

44

1 (a) 80 (b) 150
(c) 100 (d) 120
(e) 200 (f) 400

2 (a) 60 (b) 60 (c) 100
(d) 200 (e) 250

3 (a) 120 (b) 300 (c) 80
(d) 90 (e) 200 (f) 500

4 (a) 40 (b) 150 (c) 160

45

1 (a) 42p (b) 64p (c) 26p
(d) 46p (e) 88p (f) 96p
(g) 39p (h) 69p (i) 84p

2 (a) 66 (b) 84 (c) 93
(d) 66 (e) 55 (f) 86
(g) 70 (h) 88 (i) 99

3 (a) 36 (b) 50 (c) 63

46

1 (a) 46p (b) 56p (c) 78p
(d) 59p (e) 76p (f) 94p

2 (a) 3 (b) 4

3 10 green and 5 brown
or 10 red and 5 green.

47

1 (a) 4 tickets (b) 10 posters
(c) 6 T-shirts (d) 8 badges

2 (a) 2 (b) 7 (c) 1
(d) 3 (e) 0 (f) 9

3 5

4 (a) 7 (b) 6
(c) 4 (d) 2
(e) 3 (f) 8

5 (a) $\frac{1}{2}$ of ***10*** = 5 (b) $\frac{1}{2}$ of **2** = 1 (c) $\frac{1}{2}$ of **20** = 10
(d) half of ***18*** = 9 (e) half of ***0*** = 0 (f) half of ***14*** = 7

48

1 (a) 3 (b) 8 (c) 5

2 (a) 70 ÷ 10 = ***7***
(b) 20 ÷ 10 = ***2***
(c) 10 ÷ 10 = ***1***
(d) 90 ÷ 10 = ***9***

3 (a) 40 ÷ 10 = ***4***
(b) 100 ÷ 10 = ***10***
(c) 0 ÷ 10 = ***0***
(d) 60 ÷ 10 = ***6***

4 (a) 2 (b) 3
(c) 7 (d) 10
(e) 0 (f) 8

5 (a) 5 (b) 4

6 (a) ***60*** ÷ 10 = 6 (b) ***10*** ÷ 10 = 1 (c) ***90*** ÷ 10 = 9

49

1 (a) 9 (b) 6
(c) 7 (d) 10

2 (a) 4 (b) 8 (c) 0
(d) 10 (e) 5 (f) 7

3 (a) 3 (b) 8
(c) 1 (d) 2

4 (a) 9 (b) 3
(c) 6 (d) 4
(e) 5

5 (a) ***10*** ÷ 5 = 2 (b) ***0*** ÷ 5 = 0
(c) ***40*** ÷ 5 = 8 (d) ***5*** ÷ 5 = 1

50

1 (a) 1 (b) 9 (c) 2 (d) 10

2 (a) 8 (b) 2 (c) 5
(d) 3 (e) 1 (f) 6

3 (a) 5 (b) 10
(c) 7 (d) 4

4 (a) ***45*** ÷ 5 = 9 (b) ***15*** ÷ 5 = 3 (c) ***30*** ÷ 5 = 6
(d) ***0*** ÷ 5 = 0 (e) ***35*** ÷ 5 = 7 (f) ***20*** ÷ 5 = 4

51

1 (a) 10 (b) 6 (c) 8

2 (a) 2 (b) 5 (c) 3
(d) 4 (e) 9 (f) 7

3 0 ÷ 3 = ***0*** 12 ÷ 3 = ***4*** 21 ÷ 3 = ***7***
3 ÷ 3 = ***1*** 15 ÷ 3 = ***5*** 24 ÷ 3 = ***8***
6 ÷ 3 = ***2*** 18 ÷ 3 = ***6*** 27 ÷ 3 = ***9***
9 ÷ 3 = ***3*** 30 ÷ 3 = ***10***

52

1 (a) 2 (b) 1 (c) 6
(d) 8 (e) 4 (f) 10

2 (a) 3 (b) 9
(c) 5 (d) 7

3 (a) 2 (b) 6
(c) 4 (d) 9

4 8

5 (a) ***15*** ÷ 3 = 5 (b) ***3*** ÷ 3 = 1 (c) ***30*** ÷ 3 = 10
(d) ***9*** ÷ 3 = 3 (e) ***21*** ÷ 3 = 7 (f) ***0*** ÷ 3 = 0

53

1 (a) 3 (b) 5 (c) 10
(d) 8 (e) 4 (f) 7

2 (a) 2 (b) 9 (c) 6
(d) 0 (e) 5 (f) 4

3 (a) 1 (b) 7
(c) 10 (d) 8
(e) 3 (f) 2

54

1 (a) 9 (b) 5 (c) 2
(d) 6 (e) 4 (f) 1

2 **(a)** 3 **(b)** 8 **(c)** 10

3 **(a)** ***24*** ÷ 4 = 6 **(b)** ***8*** ÷ 4 = 2 **(c)** ***0*** ÷ 4 = 0
(d) ***20*** ÷ 4 = 5 **(e)** ***28*** ÷ 4 = 7 **(f)** ***4*** ÷ 4 = 1

4 40 ÷ 4 = ***10*** + 6 = ***16*** ÷ 4 = ***4*** × 10 = ***40*** – 4 = ***36*** ÷ 4 = ***9***
Car 9 wins the race.

55

1 **(a)** 5 **(b)** 4
(c) 4 **(d)** 5
(e) 9 **(f)** 6

2 **(a)** 2 **(b)** 1
(c) 9 **(d)** 8
(e) 10 **(f)** 7

3 **(a)** 6 **(b)** 2 **(c)** 9
(d) 2 **(e)** 0 **(f)** 8

4 12 or 24 balls.

56

1 **(a)** 8 **(b)** 4
(c) 9 **(d)** 6
(e) 4 **(f)** 10

2 **(a)** ***80*** ÷ 10 = 8 **(b)** ***36*** ÷ 4 = 9 **(c)** ***6*** ÷ 3 = 2
(d) ***5*** ÷ 5 = 1 **(e)** ***0*** ÷ 2 = 0 **(f)** ***30*** ÷ 10 = 3

3 **(a)** 7 **(b)** 10
(c) 4 **(d)** 2
(e) 7 **(f)** 3
(g) 7 **(h)** 8

4 **(a)** 6 **(b)** 3 **(c)** $\frac{1}{4}$ or $\frac{3}{12}$

57

1 **(a)** 24 **(b)** 12
(c) 32 **(d)** 16
(e) 40 **(f)** 20

2 **(a)** 18 **(b)** 14 **(c)** 17
(d) 11 **(e)** 15 **(f)** 13

3 **(a)** 50
(b) 25
(c) 35 **(d)** 40 **(e)** 50

4 **(a)** 100 **(b)** 300
(c) 400 **(d)** 150
(e) 250 **(f)** 350
(g) 500 **(h)** 900

58

1 **(a)** 5 × 4 = ***20***
20 ÷ 4 = ***5***
20 ÷ 5 = ***4***

(b) 5 × 10 = ***50***
10 × ***5*** = 50
50 ÷ 5 = ***10***
50 ÷ ***10*** = 5

(c) 6 ÷ ***3*** = 2
2 × 3 = ***6***
3 × ***2*** = ***6***

(d) 15 ÷ 3 = ***5***
15 ÷ ***5*** = ***3***
3 × ***5*** = 15
5 × 3 = ***15***

2 **(a)** 20 ÷ 10 = 2
20 ÷ 2 = 10

(b) 12 ÷ 3 = 4
12 ÷ 4 = 3

(c) 8 ÷ 4 = 2
8 ÷ 2 = 4

3 **(a)** 2 × 5 = 10
5 × 2 = 10
10 ÷ 2 = 5
10 ÷ 5 = 2

(b) 4 × 10 = 40
10 × 4 = 40
40 ÷ 4 = 10
40 ÷ 10 = 4

59

1 **(a)** 4 **(b)** 3

2 **(a)** 5 each, remainder 3 **(b)** 5 each, remainder 4

3 **(a)** 8 teams **(b)** 9 teams

4 **(a)** 17 **(b)** 23 **(c)** 14

5 Any remainder clue for 29
eg. divide me by 2 and my remainder is 9.

60

1 **(a)** 6 teams **(b)** 7 tables

2 5 children

3 8 pairs

4 7 dominoes

5 9 shelves

61

1 **(a)** £2·32 **(b)** £3·66
(c) £3·44 **(d)** £4·57

2 Bob

3 **(a)** Any coins totalling £2·35 e.g. £2, 20p, 10p, 5p
(b) Any coins totalling £4·73 e.g. £2, £2, 50p, 20p, 2p, 1p
(c) Any coins totalling £1·88 e.g. £1, 50p, 20p, 10p, 5p, 2p, 1p

62

1 **(a)** 2 **(b)** 20 **(c)** 10 **(d)** 4

2 **(a)** £3·55 **(b)** £5·54

3 **(a)** £2, 50p, 20p, 10p
(b) £2, £2, £1, 20p, 20p, 2p, 1p
(c) £2, £2, £2, £2, £1, 50p, 10p, 5p
(d) £2, £2, £2, £1, 50p, 20p, 20p, 5p, 2p, 1p

4 **(a)** vase **(b)** clock

5 Any four ways from those listed below:
£2, £2, £1
£2, £2, 50p, 50p
£2, £2, 50p, 20p, 20p, 10p
£2, £1, £1, 50p, 50p
£2, £1, £1, 50p, 20p, 20p, 10p

63

1 **(a)** £3·92 **(b)** £6·57 **(c)** £4·05
(d) £2·13 **(e)** £8·60 **(f)** £4·42 **(g)** £1·31
(h) £9·50 **(i)** £7·28 **(j)** £5·04 **(k)** £0·96

2 **(a)** 248p **(b)** 504p **(c)** 57p
(d) 935p **(e)** 361p **(f)** 153p **(g)** 629p
(h) 570p **(i)** 806p **(j)** 790p **(k)** 400p

3 **(a)** yellow bank **(b)** red bank

64

1 **(a)** Any coins totalling 75p, e.g. 50p, 20p, 5p
(b) Any coins totalling 37p, e.g. 20p, 10p, 5p, 2p
(c) Any coins totalling 23p, e.g. 20p, 2p, 1p

2 **(a)** Any coins totalling 68p, e.g. 50p, 10p, 5p, 2p, 1p
(b) Any coins totalling 95p, e.g. 50p, 20p, 20p, 5p
(c) Any coins totalling £1·14, e.g. £1, 10p, 2p, 2p

3 **(a)** 60p **(b)** £1·50 **(c)** 51p

4 **(a)** 20p **(b)** 20p

5 65p

65

1 Tim £9·50 Zoe £15·52
Mia £19·07 Jack £17·75

2 **(a)** Any notes and coins totalling £6·25, e.g. £5, £1, 20p, 5p
(b) Any notes and coins totalling £10·69, e.g. £10, 50p, 10p, 5p, 2p, 2p
(c) Any notes and coins totalling £17·10, e.g. £10, £5, £2, 10p
(d) Any notes and coins totalling £19·70, e.g. £10, £5, £2, £2, 50p, 20p

3 Any price between £6.26 and £10.68 inclusive.

66

1 Mel £24·10 Ben £25·96
Ella £36·82 Rob £36·20

2 **(a)** Any notes and coins totalling £22·30, e.g. £20, £2, 20p, 10p
(b) Any notes and coins totalling £26·55, e.g. £20, £5, £1, 50p, 5p
(c) Any notes and coins totalling £30·62, e.g. £20, £10, 50p, 10p, 2p
(d) Any notes and coins totalling £35·90, e.g. £20, £10, £5, 50p, 20p, 20p

67

1 **(a)** Any coins totalling £1·50, e.g. £1, 50p
(b) Any coins totalling £2·70, e.g. £2, 50p, 20p
(c) Any coins totalling £3·10, e.g. £2, £1, 10p
(d) Any coins totalling £2·40, e.g. £2, 20p, 20p
(e) Any coins totalling £2·25, e.g. £2, 20p, 5p
(f) Any coins totalling £1·80, e.g. £1, 50p, 20p, 10p

2 **(a)** £1·90 **(b)** £1·90 **(c)** £2·70
(d) £3·80 **(e)** £1·10 **(f)** £1·60

3 Class 1 needs £3·40
Class 2 needs £3·10
Class 3 needs £2·50
Class 4 needs £1·90
Class 5 needs £0·80
Class 6 needs £0·30

68

1 **(a)** Wizzo £1·50 **(b)** Pop week £1·80 **(c)** Monster £1·80
(d) Footie £7·00

2 **(a)** 10 weeks **(b)** 15 weeks **(c)** 20 weeks

3 94p

4 brown book 90p
blue book £4·00
green book £2·80

red book £1.40

69

1 (a) any of 50p, 20p, 2p, 1p, 1p
50p, 10p, 10p, 2p, 2p
(b) any of 20p, 20p, 20p, 5p, 1p
50p, 10p, 2p, 2p, 2p
50p, 5p, 5p, 5p, 1p
(c) any of £1, 20p, 5p, 1p, 1p
£1, 10p, 10p, 5p, 2p
50p, 50p, 20p, 5p, 2p
(d) any of £2, 50p, 5p, 5p, 1p
£2, 20p, 20p, 20p, 1p
£1, £1, 50p, 10p, 1p

2 (a) Paul has £1·85, Salma has £3·53.
(b) Other sets of five coins with correct totals.

3 (a) Fish and salad
(b) Burger, pizza and curry
(or burger, fish, fish)
(c) Burger and curry
(or curry, salad and salad)
(d) 10p

70

1 (a) $\frac{1}{2}$ **(b)** $\frac{1}{4}$ **(c)** 1
(d) $\frac{3}{4}$ **(e)** $\frac{1}{2}$ or (or $\frac{2}{4}$) **(f)** 1

2 1 piece of apple pie
2 pieces of plum pie
3 pieces of cherry pie
4 pieces of bramble pie

3 (a) 11 **(b)** 5 **(c)** 12 **(d)** 9
(e) 15 **(f)** 8 **(g)** 13 **(h)** 7

4 (a) 20 **(b)** 10 **(c)** 30

71

1 (a) 2 **(b)** $\frac{1}{2}$
(c) $2\frac{1}{2}$ **(d)** $3\frac{1}{2}$
(e) $4\frac{1}{2}$ **(f)** $3\frac{1}{4}$

2 (a) $0, \frac{1}{2}, 1, 1\frac{1}{2}, 2, 2\frac{1}{2}, 3$ **(b)** $2, 2\frac{1}{2}, 3, 3\frac{1}{2}, 4, 4\frac{1}{2}, 5$
(c) $7, 6\frac{1}{2}, 6, 5\frac{1}{2}, 5, 4\frac{1}{2}, 4$ **(d)** $4, 3\frac{1}{2}, 3, 2\frac{1}{2}, 2, 1\frac{1}{2}, 1$

3 Ali and Jill

72

1 (a) 2 each 4 each
(b) 2 4
(c) they are the same

2 (a) 3 **(b)** 9 **(c)** 1
(d) 5 **(e)** 7 **(f)** 10

3 (a) $\frac{5}{10}$ or $\frac{1}{2}$ **(b)** $\frac{2}{10}$ or $\frac{1}{5}$ **(c)** $\frac{3}{10}$

4 72

73

1 (a) 24 **(b)** 30 **(c)** 36 **(d)** 38 **(e)** 100
(f) 60 **(g)** 70 **(h)** 40 **(i)** 90 **(j)** 200

2 60, 120
70, 140
85, 170
55, 110
95, 190
90, 180
65, 130
75, 150
80, 160

3 **(a)** 49 **(b)** 51
(c) 32 **(d)** 36
(e) 29 **(f)** 71 **(g)** 30 **(h)** 102

4 **(a)** 170 **(b)** 190
(c) 115 **(d)** 125
(e) 150 **(f)** 110 **(g)** 95 **(h)** 195

74

1 **(a)** 120 **(b)** 110 **(c)** 140

2 **(a)** 160 **(b)** 120 **(c)** 140
(d) 30 + ***90*** = 120 **(e)** ***70*** + 60 = 130 **(f)** 70 + ***40*** = 110

3 **(a)** 101 **(b)** 124 **(c)** 121
(d) 106 **(e)** 108 **(f)** 129

4 **(a)** 133 **(b)** 102 **(c)** 125
(d) 127 **(e)** 88 **(f)** 146

5 **(a)** 84 + ***20*** = 104
(b) ***40*** + 99 = 139

75

1 **(a)** 119 **(b)** 108 **(c)** 146

2 Cal has 142 stamps. Lori has 140 stamps. Cal has more stamps.

3 **(a)** 111 **(b)** 122 **(c)** 142

4 **(a)** 137 **(b)** 107 **(c)** 110
(d) 119 **(e)** 136 **(f)** 112
(g) 134 **(h)** 121 **(i)** 143

76

1 **(a)** 328 **(b)** 409 **(c)** 560

2 **(a)** 156 **(b)** 139 **(c)** 318

3 **(a)** 417 **(b)** 506 **(c)** 250

4 **(a)** 209 **(b)** 849 **(c)** 120
(d) 759 **(e)** 430

5 **(a)** 332 **(b)** 157 **(c)** 222

6 **(a)** 423 **(b)** 533 **(c)** 611

7 **(a)** 225 **(b)** 161
(c) 546
(d) 504 **(e)** 306

77

1 **(a)** 356 **(b)** 358
(c) 272 **(d)** 274
(e) 424 **(f)** 426
(g) 615 **(h)** 904
(i) 733 **(j)** 769
(k) 701 **(l)** 290

2 161 knights

3 Ralf has 519 coins.
Coll has 508 coins.
Max has 517 coins.

78

1 **(a)** 990 **(b)** 540
(c) 890 **(d)** 790

2 **(a)** 370 **(b)** 290 **(c)** 500
(d) 780 **(e)** 700

3 **(a)** 540 + ***60*** = 600 **(b)** 720 + ***80*** = 800 **(c)** 350 + ***50*** = 400
(d) ***10*** + 890 = 900 **(e)** ***30*** + 670 = 700 **(f)** ***40*** + 460 = 500

4 **(a)** 287 **(b)** 338 **(c)** 599
(d) 197 **(e)** 242 **(f)** 194
(g) 387 **(h)** 686

79

1 Yellow: 900 Red: 800
Purple: 700 Brown: 500
Blue: 900 Green: 800

2 **(a)** 500 + ***500*** **(b)** 300 + ***700*** **(c)** 200 + ***800***
(d) ***900*** + 100 **(e)** ***400*** + 600
(f) 800 + ***200*** **(g)** 900 + ***100***
(h) 700 + ***300*** **(i)** ***600*** + 400 **(j)** Any 3 numbers totalling 1000

3 **(a)** 347 **(b)** 111 **(c)** 999
(d) 545 **(e)** 886 **(f)** 402
(g) 837 **(h)** 891 **(i)** 988

4 **(a)** 57 + ***800*** = 857 **(b)** 400 + ***509*** = 909 **(c)** ***400*** + 155 = 555

80

1 **(a)** 327 **(b)** 267
(c) 345 **(d)** 249
(e) 369

2 319

3 **(a)** 479 **(b)** 175 **(c)** 799
(d) 244 **(e)** 998 **(f)** 893
(g) 587 **(h)** 256

81

1 95 runners

2 **(a)** 293 **(b)** 491 **(c)** 594 **(d)** 390
(e) 698 **(f)** 900 **(g)** 192 **(h)** 799

3 97 spectators

4 **(a)** 96 **(b)** 80 **(c)** 71
(d) 90 **(e)** 86 **(f)** 15

5 **(a)** 120 – ***80*** = 40 **(b)** 114 – ***20*** = 94

82

1 **(a)** 249 **(b)** 247
(c) 316 **(d)** 314
(e) 393 **(f)** 391
(g) 324 **(h)** 206
(i) 191 **(j)** 489

2 **(a)** 185 **(b)** 115

3 **(a)** £98 **(b)** £96

83

1 **(a)** £300 **(b)** £100

2 **(a)** £200 **(b)** £300 **(c)** £500

3 **(a)** 300 **(b)** 200 **(c)** 100

4 Pam has £309 left.
Rod has £473 left.

5 **(a)** 427 **(b)** 199 **(c)** 340
(d) 444 **(e)** 206 **(f)** 12

6 **(a)** 900 – ***700*** = 200 **(b)** ***485*** – 100 = 385
(c) ***937*** – 700 = 237 **(d)** 586 – ***400*** = 186

84

1 **(a)** 6 cm **(b)** 3 cm

2 **(a)** 4 cm **(b)** 5 cm

3 **(a)** 4 **(b)** 6 **(c)** 6
(d) 3 **(e)** 5 **(f)** 6

4 **(a)** 5 m **(b)** 8 m
(c) 7 m **(d)** 6 m

5 **(a)** 7 **(b)** 6 **(c)** 4
(d) 5 **(e)** 8 **(f)** 7

6 **(a)** 563 – ***7*** = 556 **(b)** 806 – ***8*** = 798 **(c)** ***303*** – 4 = 299

85

1 804 seats

2 **(a)** 440 tickets **(b)** 5 tickets

3 99 tickets

4 **(a)** 149 **(b)** 80

5 197

86

1 *practical work*

2 The sand weighs more than 1 kg.
The pebbles weigh less than $2\frac{1}{2}$ kg.
The shells weigh less than $1\frac{1}{2}$ kg.
The pumpkin weighs less than 2 kg.
The flour weighs less than 1 kg.
The bananas weigh $2\frac{1}{2}$ kg.

3 Any object weighing between 2 kg and 3 kg.

87

1 **(a)** 2 kg **(b)** $2\frac{1}{2}$ kg *and* 2 kg 500 g
(c) $\frac{1}{2}$ kg *and* 500 g **(d)** $3\frac{1}{2}$ kg *and* 3 kg 500 g

2 *practical work*

3 *practical work*

88

1 **(a)** soap powder pasta dog food

(b) beans cornflakes biscuits

2 **(a)** cornflakes and biscuits
(b) cornflakes and pasta
(c) beans and soap powder

3 pasta, beans and biscuits

4 **(a)** 100 g **(b)** 30 kg
(c) 3 kg **(d)** 500 g

5 **(a)** 20 kg **(b)** 3 kg

89

practical work

90

practical work

91

1 **(a)** 14 cm **(b)** 9 cm **(c)** $11\frac{1}{2}$ cm
(d) $15\frac{1}{2}$ cm **(e)** 8 cm **(f)** 13 cm

2 **(a)** 7 cm **(b)** 5 cm **(c)** $2\frac{1}{2}$ cm
(d) $11\frac{1}{2}$ cm **(e)** $4\frac{1}{2}$ cm

3 **(a)** line drawn of 10 cm **(b)** line drawn of $3\frac{1}{2}$ cm
(c) line drawn of 6 cm **(d)** line drawn of $12\frac{1}{2}$ cm

92

practical work

93

1 **(a)** about 8 counters **(b)** about 7 counters
(c) about 10 counters **(d)** about 7 counters

2 **(a)** dog **(b)** baby

3 *practical work*

94

1 **(a)** 12 squares **(b)** 19 squares
(c) 16 squares **(d)** 13 squares

2 **(a)** shape b **(b)** shape a

3 **(a)** shape drawn with area of 10 squares
(b) shape drawn with area of 20 squares
(c) shape drawn with area of 30 squares

4 2 different shapes drawn, each with an area of 24 squares.

95

practical work

96

1 **(a)** 57 litres **(b)** 78 litres **(c)** 99 litres

2 **(a)** 6 litres **(b)** 15 litres **(c)** 21 litres

3 Any of:

- Fill the 1 litre jug and pour it into the basin. Do this 3 times.
- Fill the 2 litre jug and the 1 litre jug. Pour them both into the basin.
- Fill the 5 litre jug and use it to fill the 2 litre jug. Pour the remainder

into the basin.

- Fill the 5 litre jug and use it to fill the 1 litre jug twice. Pour the remainder into the basin.

4 **(a)** 10 **(b)** 5

5 5 200 ml bottles
4 200 ml bottles and 2 100 ml bottles
3 200 ml bottles and 4 100 ml bottles
2 200 ml bottles and 6 100 ml bottles
1 200 ml bottle and 8 100 ml bottles
10 100 ml bottles

97

1 **(a)** 4 **(b)** 5

2 **(a)** Tuesday **(b)** Monday **(c)** Friday

3 **(a)** Friday **(b)** Friday
(c) Saturday **(d)** Tuesday

4 **(a)** 15th July **(b)** 31st July

5 Saturday

6 **(a)** January, March, May, July, August, October, December
(b) April, June, September, November

7 The day of the week these dates fall on *this* year.
(a) 25th December **(b)** 1st April **(c)** 1st January

98

1 **(a)** quarter past 1 **(b)** quarter to 11 **(c)** half past 7
(d) 11 o'clock **(e)** quarter to 6 **(f)** quarter past 12

2 **(a)** quarter past 8
(b) half past 6
(c) 3 o'clock
(d) quarter past 9
(e) quarter to 4
(f) quarter past 11
(g) 10 o'clock
(h) quarter to 3

99

1 **(a)** 2.00 **(b)** 11.45 **(c)** 6.15
(d) 4.15 **(e)** 12.30 **(f)** 5.00
(g) 7.45 **(h)** 1.30 **(i)** 2.15

2 **(a)** 5.15 **(b)** 10.00 or 10 o'clock

3 6.30 7.15 7.45 8.00

100

1 **(a)** on the bus, at the farm, in the park
(b) eating their snack, at the pond, back to school.

2 **(a)** 10.15 pm **(b)** 8.00 am **(c)** 3.30 pm
(d) 10.45 am **(e)** 4.00 pm

3 **(a)** Drawing of 2 things done before 10.30 am
(b) Drawing of 2 things done after 4.45 pm

101

1 **(a)** 2.25 **(b)** 9.30 **(c)** 3.05
(d) 6.15 **(e)** 10.00 **(f)** 11.50
(g) 2.20 **(h)** 10.35
(i) 5.50 **(j)** 8.55

(k) 3.45 **(l)** 7.10

2 6.40 7.35 8.25 8.30 9.05 9.20

102

1 **(a)** 11.10 **(b)** 25 minutes to 2
(c) 20 minutes past 2 **(d)** 2.35
(e) 4.00 **(f)** 5.05
(g) 6.50 **(h)** 5 minutes to 9

2 Sally: red Alma: blue Tony: green

103

1 20 minutes between A and B
5 minutes between B and C
25 minutes between C and D
30 minutes between D and E
40 minutes between E and F

2 25 minutes

3 30 minutes

4 2 hours

5 **(a)** crossing the bridge **(b)** in the park

104

1 8.50 am

2 40 minutes

3 10.30 am

4 **(a)** 1.30 pm **(b)** 30 minutes **(c)** 2.40 pm

5 6.05 pm

105

1 **(a)** cube, cone, sphere, triangular prism, cylinder, cuboid, square based pyramid
(b) cube, cylinder, cuboid, triangular prism

2 **(a)** cone **(b)** cube **(c)** cylinder **(d)** triangular prism

3 **(a)** clues describing sphere
(b) clues describing square based pyramid

106

1 *practical work*

2 shapes a c d

3 **(a)** *practical work*
(b) Sketch of a prism
(c) Sketch of a different prism

107

1 *practical work*

2

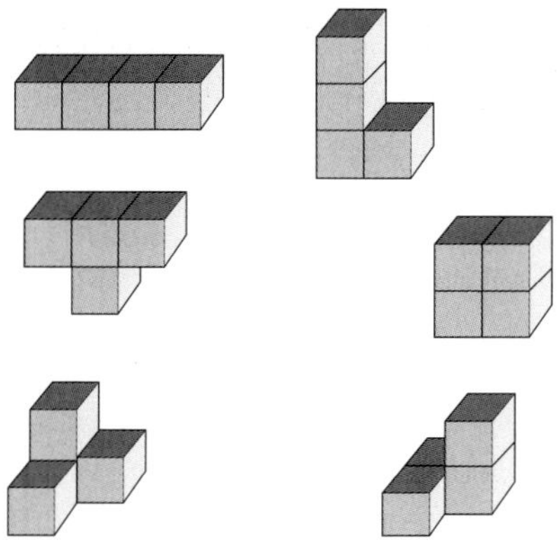

3 *practical work*

108

1 *practical work*

2 (a)

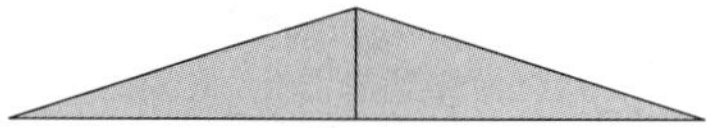

(b)

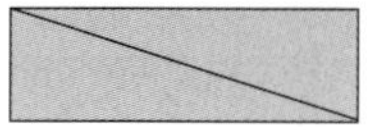

or

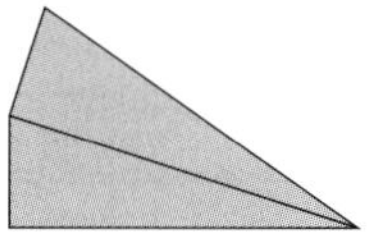

(c) any six sided shape
eg.

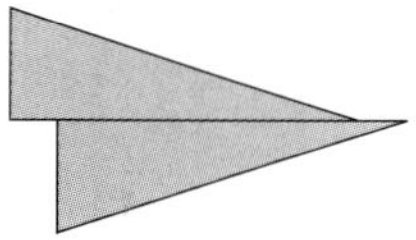

(d) any five sided shape
eg.

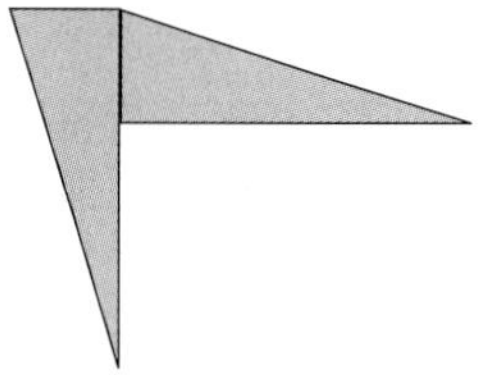

3 *practical work*

4 (a)

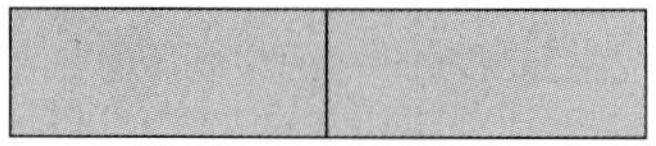

(b) any eight sided shape
eg.

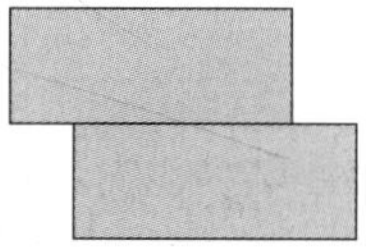

5 (a)

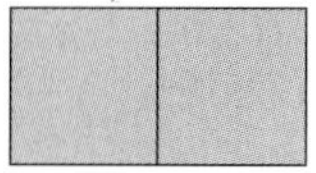

(b)

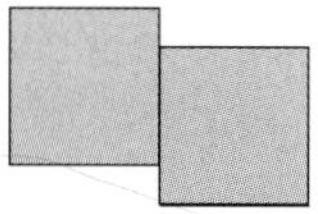

109

1 (a) castle tower **(b)** hut **(c)** pick axe

2 (a) B4 **(b)** F4 **(c)** F2 **(d)** C1, D1 **(e)** C3, D3

3 A4, B2, F1

4 B3, C3, C4, D4, E4, E3, E2, D2

110

1 (a) island **(b)** whale

2 (a) South **(b)** West

3 (a) whale **(b)** volcano
(c) raft **(d)** island

4 (a) South **(b)** South
(c) East **(d)** East

5 An island with features as in the diagram.

wood

hills lake

tower

111

1 **(a)** 2 **(b)** 2 **(c)** 1
(d) 1 **(e)** 0 **(f)** 2

2 K has 1 line of symmetry
I has 2 lines of symmetry
F has 0 lines of symmetry

3 shape b

4 shape b

112

1 **(a)** Theme Park was most popular.
Safari Park was least popular.

(b) The Water and Theme Parks had more than 7 votes.
The Safari Park had less than 7 votes.

(c) 12 children

2 *practical work*

113

1 **(a)** 7 **(b)** 3
(c) 9 **(d)** 25

2 **(a)** 4 **(b)** 3 **(c)** 2

3 **(a)** Slimy **(b)** Scary
(c) Creepy **(d)** Slimy
(e) Creepy **(f)** Slimy

114

1 Swing Boat

2 **(a)** Roller Coaster
(b) Log Flume
(c) Big Wheel
(d) Parachute

3 **(a)** 2 minutes **(b)** 9 minutes **(c)** 6 minutes

4 Some rides are more popular than others.
The queues are different lengths.

115

1 **(a)** V-neck **(b)** collar

2 **(a)** 8 children **(b)** 10 children
(c) 5 children **(d)** 9 children

3 32 childen

4 V-neck

5 **(a)** 12 **(b)** 6 **(c)** 3 **(d)** 11

6 **(a)** striped **(b)** checked

116

1 **(a)** *practical work*

(b)

4 sides	not 4 sides
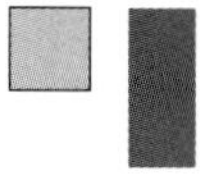	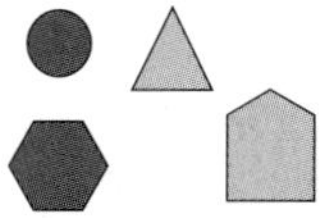

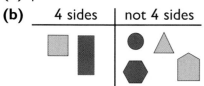

(c) square and rectangle (and any other quadrilateral)

2 **(a)** *practical work*

(b)

	4 vertices	not 4 vertices
all sides same length		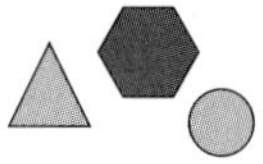
all sides not same length		

(c) square

any shape with unequal sides eg. irregular pentagon.

117

1 **(a)**

- any three of 0, 15, 20, 35, 40, 45, 50
- any number greater than 50 which is not a multiple of 5 (other than 73, 87, 51, 98).
- any multiple of 5 that is greater than 50, other than 65 and 80.

(b) 50 should go in the yellow part – it is a multiple of 5 but is not greater than 50.

2 Their own Venn diagram.

(d) Numbers that were less than 20 or more than 60 that were not multiples of 4.

They were in neither category.

E1

1 **(a)** 1000, 2000, 3000, **4000**, **5000**, **6000**
(b) 5000, 6000, **7000**, **8000**, 9000, **10 000**
(c) 1500, 2500, **3500**, **4500**, 5500, **6500**
(d) 100, 1100, **2100**, **3100**, **4100**, 5100
(e) **200**, **1200**, 2200, **3200**, 4200, 5200
(f) **10 000**, **9000**, **8000**, 7000, 6000, **5000**
(g) **8400**, **7400**, 6400, **5400**, **4400**, 3400

2 **(a)** 3800, 4800, 5800, 6800, 7800, 8800, 9800
(b) 6300, 5300, 4300, 3300, 2300, 1300, 300

3 **(a)** 3300 **(b)** 6200 **(c)** 1800 **(d)** 10 000

4 **(a)** 6900 **(b)** 5400 **(c)** 9000 **(d)** 500

5 **(a)** 3000 **(b)** 6000 **(c)** 9000 **(d)** 5000

E2

1 **(a)** 700, 800, **900**, **1000**, 1100, **1200**
(b) **7500**, 7600, 7700, **7800**, 7900, **8000**
(c) 3700, 3800, **3900**, **4000**, **4100**, 4200
(d) **4800**, 4900, **5000**, **5100**, 5200, **5300**
(e) 6800, 6700, **6600**, **6500**, **6400**, 6300
(f) 7300, 7200, **7100**, **7000**, **6900**, **6800**
(g) **10 000**, 9900, 9800, **9700**, **9600**, 9500

2 **(a)** 3200, 3300, 3400, 3500, 3600, 3700, 3800, 3900, 4000
(b) 6400, 6300, 6200, 6100, 6000, 5900, 5800

3 **(a)** 2700 **(b)** 7100 **(c)** 7000 **(d)** 10 000

4 **(a)** 5200 **(b)** 1900 **(c)** 9900 **(d)** 8000

5 **(a)** 1400 **(b)** 1700 **(c)** 1300 **(d)** 2000

E3

1 A = 45
B = 75
C = 80
D = 95
E = 65
F = 15
G = 50

2 All the numbers are multiples of 5.

E4

1

$2 \times \mathbf{8} = 16$	$5 \times \mathbf{5} = 25$	$4 \times \mathbf{4} = 16$	$10 \times \mathbf{4} = 40$	$3 \times \mathbf{7} = 21$
H	E	L	L	O
$5 \times \mathbf{2} = 10$	$0 \times \mathbf{4} = 0$	$10 \times \mathbf{7} = 70$	$3 \times \mathbf{9} = 27$	$5 \times \mathbf{8} = 40$
E	A	R	T	H
$2 \times \mathbf{10} = 20$	$4 \times \mathbf{8} = 32$	$3 \times \mathbf{6} = 18$	$2 \times \mathbf{4} = 8$	
C	H	I	L	
$1 \times \mathbf{5} = 5$	$7 \times \mathbf{2} = 14$	$4 \times \mathbf{5} = 20$	$3 \times \mathbf{10} = 30$	
D	R	E	N	

Hello Earth Children

2 10, 0, 9 NAT

E5

1 Max £32·60
Sue £32·35
Roy £34·75

Mia £35·90
Cal £33·30

2 **(a)** Sue **(b)** Max

3 **(a)** 25p **(b)** £2·60

4 **(a)** 95p **(b)** £2·15

5 £7·65

6 **(a)** £31·80 **(b)** £37·00

E6

1 £1·30

2 19 badges

3 25 pens each

4 **(a)** 6 cards **(b)** They each have 1p left.

E7

Game

E8

1 **(a)** 5 **(b)** 7

2 **(a)** 9 **(b)** 1 **(c)** 10
(d) 4 **(e)** 8 **(f)** 2

3 **(a)** Practical work

(b) •3 cubes are red •6 cubes are yellow.

4 **(a)** Practical work

(b) •6 cubes are blue •12 cubes are not blue.

5 15 cubes altogether.

E9

1 **(a)** 2 apples 5 strawberries 3 pears 6 plums
(b) 2 apples 5 strawberries 3 pears 6 plums
(c) They give the same answers.

2 **(a)** 9 **(b)** 4 **(c)** 7
(d) 8 **(e)** 1 **(f)** 6

3 Three fifths are ripe.

4 **(a)** Four fifths are not bad.

(b) •10 apples are bad •40 apples are not.

E10

1 **(a)** 456 **(b)** 369
(c) 294 **(d)** 577
(e) 248 **(f)** 386

2 **(a)** 477 **(b)** 699 **(c)** 750
(d) 666 **(e)** 929 **(f)** 797

3 **(a)** £239 **(b)** £392 **(c)** £554

4 New York and Paris

E11

1 **(a)** 194
(b) 293
(c) 271
(d) 483
(e) 935

2 **(a)** 564 **(b)** 812 **(c)** 552 **(d)** 862

3 **(a)** 788 **(b)** 617 **(c)** 907 **(d)** 568

4 **(a)** 597 pages **(b)** 619 pages

E12

1 **(a)** £44 **(b)** £209 **(c)** £340
(d) £53 **(e)** £110 **(f)** £31

2 **(a)** 634 **(b)** 231 **(c)** 442
(d) 113 **(e)** 222 **(f)** 704
(g) 522 **(h)** 140 **(i)** 50

3 £375

E13

1 **(a)** 106 **(b)** 109
(c) 107 **(d)** 218
(e) 225 **(f)** 328

2 **(a)** 658 **(b)** 415 **(c)** 239
(d) 259 **(e)** 115 **(f)** 236

3 **(a)** £202 **(b)** £339

4 **(a)** £317 **(b)** £224

E14

1 **(a)** £1500 **(b)** £1300 **(c)** £1700
(d) £1700 **(e)** £4000 **(f)** £1600

2 **(a)** £300 **(b)** £700 **(c)** £1000
(d) £600 **(e)** £2000 **(f)** £200

3 **(a)** £4 **(b)** £9

E15

1 **(a)** Jack is about 120 **centimetres** tall.
(b) He weighs about 30 **kilograms**.
(c) The distance from Jack's house to his school is about 1 **kilometre**.
(d) It takes him about 20 **minutes** to walk to school.
(e) The school bell rings at 9 **o'clock**. (or 9 **am**.)
(f) Jack's pet rat weighs about 600 **grams**.
(g) Jack drinks about 2 **litres** of water each day.
(h) He goes to bed at 8.30 **pm**.
(i) His bed is about 2 **metres** long.

2 4 similar sentences using correct units.

E16

1 **(a)** 9.55 am **(b)** £1·00
(c) 1 hour 10 minutes **(d)** £1·40
(e) 1.20 pm **(f)** £3·60
(g) 2 hours **(h)** 4.00 pm

2 **(a)** 16 squares **(b)** 13 squares

3 **(a)** 2 lines of symmetry **(b)** 0 lines of symmetry

4 Drawing of shape, including some half squares. Correct calculation of its area.

E17

1 **(a)** 95 **(b)** 130 **(c)** 35 **(d)** 53
(e) centimetres **(f)** days **(g)** grams **(h)** millilitres
(i) octagon **(j)** triangular prism **(k)** East

2 Similar clues.

E18–19

1 **(a)** A-osaur, F-osaur, H-osaur
(b) A-osaur, D-osaur, E-osaur, F-osaur, G-osaur, I-osaur
(c) D-osaur, F-osaur, G-osaur
(d) A-osaur, E-osaur, I-osaur
(e) D-osaur, F-osaur, G-osaur
(f) B-osaur, C-osaur, H-osaur

2 **(a)** F-osaur **(b)** C-osaur
(c) I-osaur **(d)** H-osaur

3

	spikes	~~spikes~~
red	C-osaur or E-osaur	G-osaur
~~red~~	A-osaur B-osaur H-osaur I-osaur	D-osaur F-osaur

E20

Practical work

E21

(a) Continuation of patterns.
(b) Own pattern of squares and rectangles.
(c) Continuation of patterns.
(d) Own pattern of triangles and rectangles.

E22

1 Practical work

2 **(a)**

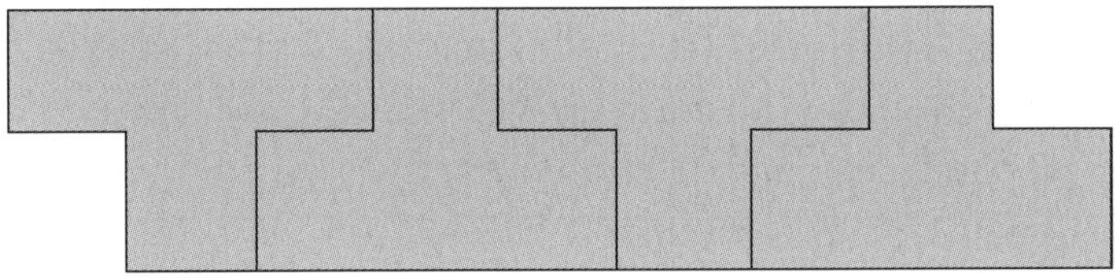

(b) Practical work

(c)

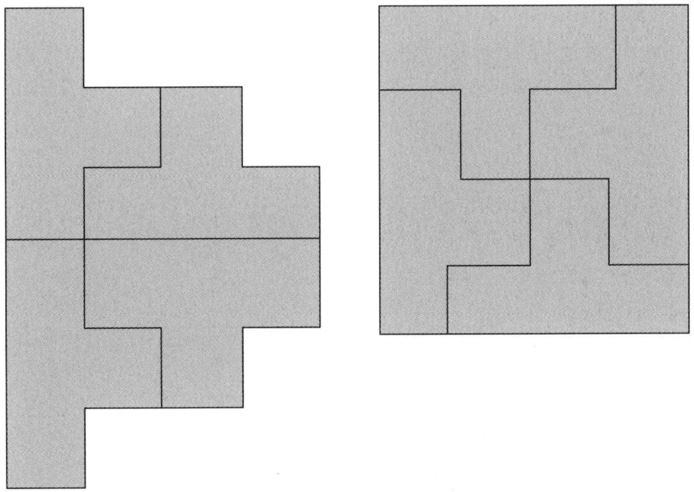

Check-up 1

Name:

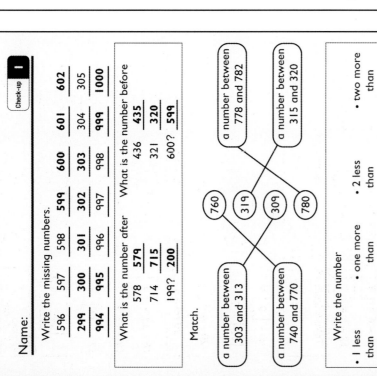

Write the missing numbers.

596	597	598	**599**	**600**	**601**	**602**
299	**300**	**301**	**302**	**303**	304	305
994	**995**	996	997	998	**999**	**1000**

What is the number after

578 **579**

714 **715**

199? **200**

What is the number before

436 **435**

321 **320**

600? **599**

Match.

a number between 303 and 313 — 309

a number between 740 and 770 — 760

a number between 778 and 782 — 780

a number between 315 and 320 — 319

Write the number

• 1 less than		• one more than		• 2 less than		• two more than	
276	**275**	672	**673**	701	**699**	808	**810**
1000	**999**	299	**300**	998	**996**	499	**501**

Check-up 2

Name:

Write the number

ten more than

444 **454** 370 **380**

605 **615** 892 **902**

10 less than

563 **553** 120 **110**

911 **901** 707 **697**

Write the number

100 more than 345 **445** 100 less than 800 **700**

100 more than 504 **604** 100 less than 636 **536**

100 more than 900 **1000** 100 less than 280 **180**

410 + 70 = **480** 537 + 30 = **567** 109 + 50 = **159**

375 – 20 = **355** 876 – 60 = **816** 543 – 40 = **503**

212 + 700 = **912** 560 + 400 = **960** 605 + 300 = **905**

950 – 500 = **450** 708 – 300 = **408** 713 – 200 = **513**

246 + **400** = 646 399 + **500** = 899 421 – **100** = 321

Check-up 3

Name:

Complete.

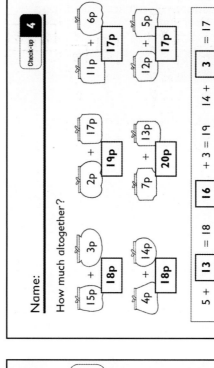

4 hundreds 6 tens and 4 units
400 + **60** + **4** = **464**

9 hundreds 5 tens and 5 units
900 + **50** + **5** = **955**

300 + 80 + 6 = **386**

400 + 0 + 7 = **407**

243 = 200 + **40** + 3

821 = **800** + **20** + **1**

730 = **700** + **30** + **0**

692 = **600** + 90 + 2

Colour the boat numbers with
- 3 hundreds and 2 units ⟶ yellow
- 5 hundreds and 3 tens ⟶ blue.

Write the numbers in order.

Start with the smallest.

792 927 729 972

729 792 927 972

Start with the largest.

684 486 864 648 468

864 684 648 486 468

Check-up 4

Name:

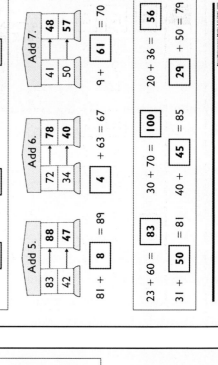

How much altogether?

15p + 3p = **18p**

2p + 17p = **19p**

11p + 6p = **17p**

4p + 14p = **18p**

7p + 13p = **20p**

12p + 5p = **17p**

5 + **13** = 18 **16** + 3 = 19 14 + **3** = 17

11 + **9** = 20 **6** + 14 = 20 8 + **12** = 20

Add 5.	
83 →	**88**
42 →	**47**

Add 6.	
72 →	**78**
34 →	**40**

Add 7.	
41 →	**48**
50 →	**57**

81 + **8** = 89 **4** + 63 = 67 9 + **61** = 70

23 + 60 = **83** 30 + 70 = **100** 20 + 36 = **56**

31 + **50** = 81 40 + **45** = 85 **29** + 50 = 79

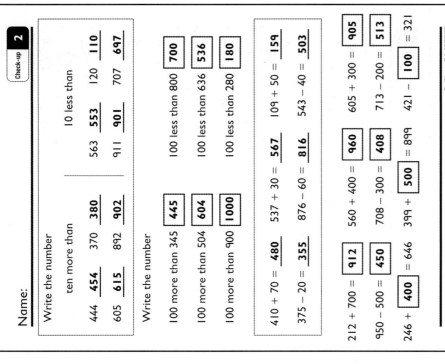

Name: **Check-up 5**

23	add 31 →	**54**	58	add 19 →	**77**
35	add 59 →	**94**	46	add 41 →	**87**
77	add 21 →	**98**	31	add 29 →	**60**

Find each total.

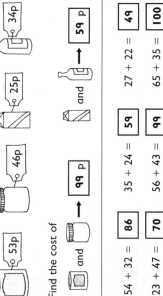

35 + 12 = **47** 43 + 16 = **59** 15 + 81 = **96**

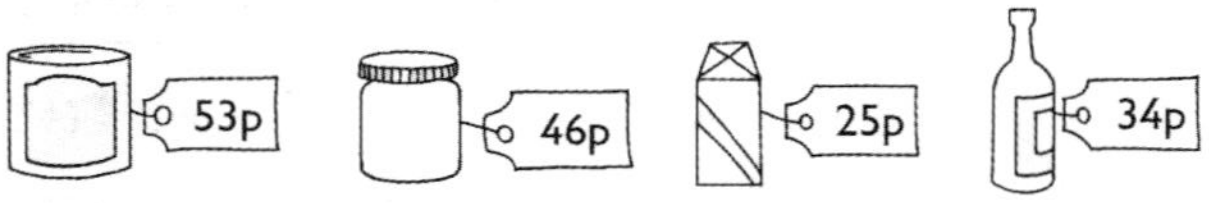

Find the cost of

and → **99** p and → **59** p

54 + 32 = **86** 35 + 24 = **59** 27 + 22 = **49**

23 + 47 = **70** 56 + 43 = **99** 65 + 35 = **100**

Name: **Check-up 6**

18 + 5 = **23** 7 + 19 = **26** 17 + 4 = **21**

What is the total of 29 and 3? **32** 65 plus 8 = **73**

Find the sum of 6 and 34. **40** Add 7 to 46. **53**

Find each total.

67 + 15 = **82** 39 + 12 = **51** 58 + **17** = 75

Add the numbers on the

cars **82** trucks **82** buses **100**

49 + 23 = **72** 26 + 47 = **73** 55 + **38** = 93

6 + 13 + 4 = **23** 14 + 11 + 7 = **32**

8 + 3 + 12 + 5 = **28** 14 + 10 + 14 + 2 = **40**

Name: **Check-up 7**

15 – 6 = **9** 13 – 7 = **6** 14 – 9 = **5**

12 – 5 = **7** 11 – 4 = **7** 16 – 8 = **8**

Take 9 from 18. **9** Subtract 6 from 11. **5**

17 minus 6 **11** 19 subtract 3 **16**

15 – **8** = 7 19 – **6** = 13 18 – **5** = 13

12 – 9 = 3 **16** – 4 = 12 **14** – 5 = 9

20 – 4 = **16** 20 – 12 = **8** 20 – 18 = **2**

20 take away 15 **5** 8 fewer than 20 **12**

16 – 13 = **3** 17 – 11 = **6** 13 – 10 = **3**

18 – 15 = **3** 19 – 16 = **3** 15 – 12 = **3**

17 – **14** = 3 14 – **13** = 1 18 – **14** = 4

Find the difference in price between

and **5** p and **3** p

Name: **Check-up 8**

58 – 7 = **51** 66 – 2 = **64** 78 – 6 = **72**

37 – 5 = **32** 85 – 3 = **82** 44 – 4 = **40**

99 subtract 8 = **91** 75 minus 4 = **71**

57 – **3** = 54 69 – **6** = 63 **36** – 5 = 31

Subtract 10 from 38. **28** Take 40 from 75. **35**

30 less than 89 = **59** 93 minus 60 = **33**

53 – 20 = **33** 94 – 70 = **24** 66 – 50 = **16**

87 – **50** = 37 72 – **30** = 42 **81** – 40 = 41

34 – 11 = **23** 56 – 21 = **35** 72 – 31 = **41**

47 – 9 = **38** 63 – 19 = **44** 95 – 49 = **46**

69 subtract 41 = **28** 84 take away 59 = **25**

82 people are on the train.

61 people get off.

How many stay on the train? **21**

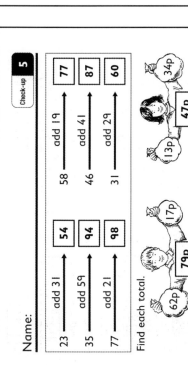

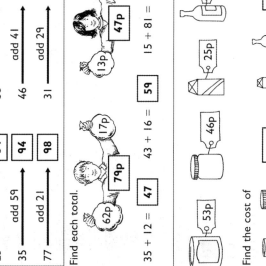

Name: **Check-up 9**

57 – 13 = **44**   49 – 16 = **33**   76 – 15 = **61**

67 – 17 = **50**   86 – 14 = **72**   35 – 12 = **23**

Take 14 from 78. **64**   Subtract 16 from 58. **42**

35 minus 13 = **22**   69 take away 18 = **51**

98 – [**27**] = 71   [**57**] – 15 = 42

99 – 36 = **63**   66 – 42 = **24**   54 – 24 = **30**

75 – 64 = **11**   87 – 55 = **32**   59 – 33 = **26**

68 – [**33**] = 35   76 – [**34**] = 42

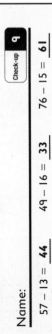

What is the difference in kilograms between the weights lifted by

- Leo and Claudio **26 kg**
- Claudio and Mario? **13 kg**

Find the difference between the heaviest and lightest weights. **35 kg**

Name: **Check-up 10**

25 – 6 = [**19**]   24 – 8 = [**16**]   22 – 7 = [**15**]

62 – 3 = [**59**]   57 – 9 = [**48**]   36 – 8 = [**28**]

21 – [**3**] = 18   43 – [**5**] = 38   78 – [**9**] = 69

38 – 19 = **19**   66 – 17 = **49**   54 – 16 = **38**

85 – 18 = **67**   92 – 14 = **78**   71 – 15 = **56**

43 – [**14**] = 29   [**60**] –13 = 47

91 – 43 = **48**

42 – 25 = **17**

80 – 48 = **32**

Find the difference between the points scored by

- Sam and Bob **37**
- Bob and Akram. **25**

How many fewer points did Ali score than Bob? **19**

Name: **Check-up 11**

2 × 8 = [**16**]   10 × 7 = [**70**]   2 × 6 = [**12**]

10 × 10 = [**100**]   9 × 2 = [**18**]   2 × 4 = [**8**]

2 × 7 = [**14**]   10 × 10 = [**100**]   8 × 10 = [**80**]

10 × [**9**] = 90   2 × [**5**] = 10   10 × [**5**] = 50

[**0**] × 2 = 0   [**4**] × 10 = 40   [**1**] × 2 = 2

10 × [**6**] = 60   [**3**] × 2 = 6   10 × [**3**] = 30

Match.

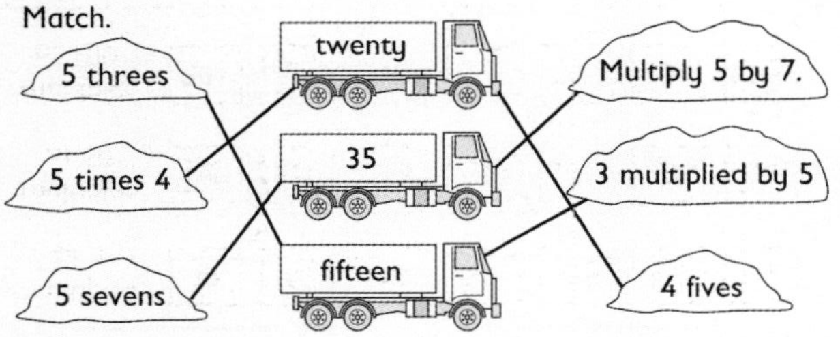

5 × 9 = [**45**]   5 × 6 = [**30**]   5 × 2 = [**10**]

5 × 0 = [**0**]   5 × 10 = [**50**]   8 × 5 = [**40**]

5 × [**5**] = 25   [**1**] × 5 = 5   5 × [**9**] = 45

Name: **Check-up 12**

How much?

3 [cakes] [**12p**]   3 [apples] [**21p**]   3 [bananas] ? [**27p**]

3 × 6 = [**18**]   5 × 3 = [**15**]   3 × 0 = [**0**]

3 × [**2**] = 6   3 × [**8**] = 24   3 × [**3**] = 9

Find the cost of

4 [mugs] **£12**   4 [balls] **£20**

3 [shorts] and 1 [mug] **£15**

8 × 4 = [**32**]   2 × 4 = [**8**]   4 × 6 = [**24**]

4 × [**10**] = 40   4 × [**1**] = 4   4 × [**7**] = 28

3 ones = [**3**]   9 multiplied by 4 = [**36**]

8 times 3 = [**24**]   4 fours = [**16**]

Multiply 10 by 3. [**30**]   0 times 4 = [**0**]

Check-up 13

Name:

Cross (×)

multiples of 2	~~36~~	23	~~38~~	~~102~~	111	~~180~~	191
multiples of 5	32	~~45~~	~~80~~	122	~~135~~	168	~~200~~
multiples of 50	~~400~~	~~650~~	205	~~900~~	170	245	~~750~~
multiples of 100.	205	~~300~~	~~100~~	650	~~200~~	160	~~1000~~

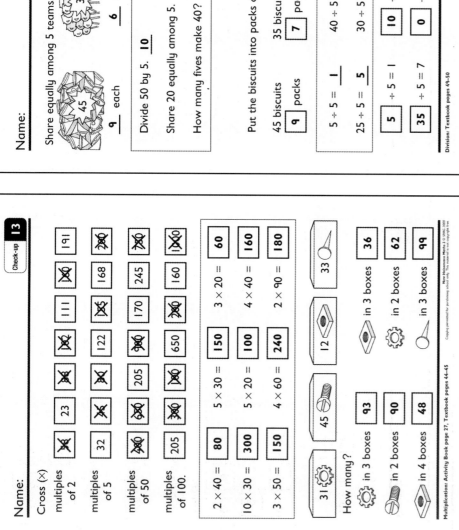

$2 \times 40 =$ **80** $5 \times 30 =$ **150** $3 \times 20 =$ **60**

$10 \times 30 =$ **300** $5 \times 20 =$ **100** $4 \times 40 =$ **160**

$3 \times 50 =$ **150** $4 \times 60 =$ **240** $2 \times 90 =$ **180**

31 | 45 | 12 | 33

How many?

in 3 boxes **93** in 3 boxes **36**

in 2 boxes **90** in 2 boxes **62**

in 4 boxes **48** in 3 boxes **99**

Check-up 14

Name:

Share equally among 5 teams.

45: **9** each 30: **6** each 15: **3** each

Divide 50 by 5. **10** 10 divided by 5 **2**

Share 20 equally among 5. **4**

How many fives make 40? **8**

Put the biscuits into packs of 5.

45 biscuits **9** packs 35 biscuits **7** packs 25 biscuits **5** packs

$5 \div 5 =$ **1** $40 \div 5 =$ **8** $15 \div 5 =$ **3**

$25 \div 5 =$ **5** $30 \div 5 =$ **6** $0 \div 5 =$ **0**

5 $\div 5 = 1$ **10** $\div 5 = 2$ **20** $\div 5 = 4$

35 $\div 5 = 7$ **0** $\div 5 = 0$ **50** $\div 5 = 10$

Check-up 15

Name:

How many jugglers can have three hoops each?

15: **5** jugglers 27: **9** jugglers

$3 \div 3 =$ **1** $24 \div 3 =$ **8** $18 \div 3 =$ **6**

$12 \div 3 =$ **4** $21 \div 3 =$ **7** $6 \div 3 =$ **2**

$30 \div 3 =$ **10** $9 \div 3 =$ **3** $0 \div 3 =$ **0**

Divide 21 by 3. **7** 15 divided by 3 **5**

30 shared equally among 3 **10**

Divide 27 equally among 3. **9**

How many threes make 9? **3**

12 $\div 3 = 4$ **18** $\div 3 = 6$ **24** $\div 3 = 8$

3 $\div 3 = 1$ **0** $\div 3 = 0$ **6** $\div 3 = 2$

Check-up 16

Name:

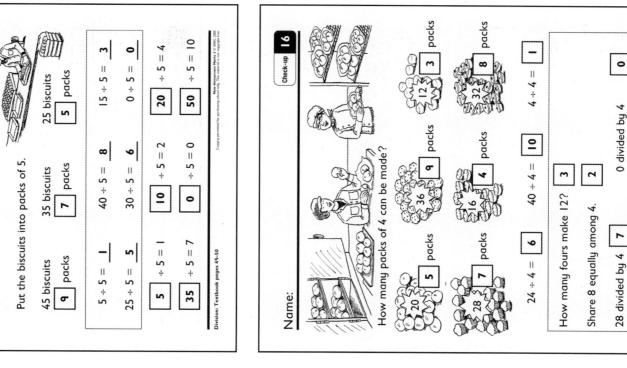

How many packs of 4 can be made?

20: **5** packs 36: **9** packs 12: **3** packs

28: **7** packs 16: **4** packs 32: **8** packs

$24 \div 4 =$ **6** $40 \div 4 =$ **10** $4 \div 4 =$ **1**

How many fours make 12? **3**

Share 8 equally among 4. **2**

28 divided by 4 **7** 0 divided by 4 **0**

Divide 36 by 4. **9** One quarter of 20 **5**

40 $\div 4 = 10$ **16** $\div 4 = 4$ **32** $\div 4 = 8$

Name: **Check-up 17**

Divide equally among the teams.

12 → 3 teams — **4** each; 16 → 2 teams — **8** each; 5 → 5 teams — **1** each

40 → 4 teams — **10** each; 20 → 10 teams — **2** each; 21 → 3 teams — **7** each

6 ÷ 2 = **3**	35 ÷ 5 = **7**	60 ÷ 10 = **6**
27 ÷ 3 = **9**	12 ÷ 4 = **3**	15 ÷ 3 = **5**
80 ÷ 10 = **8**	20 ÷ 5 = **4**	0 ÷ 4 = **0**
8 ÷ 4 = 2	**14** ÷ 2 = 7	**100** ÷ 10 = 10

Share 20 equally between 2. **10**

How many groups of 10 in 40? **4**

Divide 45 by 5. **9** — 18 divided by 3 **6**

Half of 18 **9** — One quarter of 24 **6**

Three of the 28 dominoes are lost. Divide the rest of the dominoes equally among 5 players.

5 dominoes each

Division: Textbook pages 55–56

Name: **Check-up 18**

How much?

£3·73

£4·45

List coins to buy each item. Use as few coins as possible.

£2·91 **£2, 50p, 20p, 20p, 1p**

£4·29 **£2, £2, 20p, 5p 2p, 2p**

£3·67 **£2, £1, 50p, 10p, 5p, 2p**

MEGA £1·08 — List the coins in your change from £2.

50p, 20p, 20p, 2p (= 92p)

Write each amount in **pounds and pence.**

485p **£4·85** — 92p **£0·92** — 640p **£6·40**

Write each amount in **pence.**

£8·38 **838p** — £5·06 **506p** — £0·70 **70p**

Money: Textbook pages 61–64

Name: **Check-up 19**

How much?

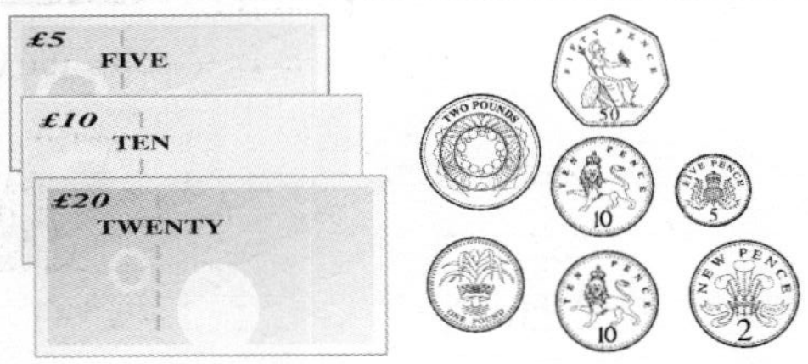

£38·77

Lay out and list notes and coins to buy each item.

£18·45 **20p 20p 5p**

£26·90 **50p 20p 20p**

List the coins in each child's change.

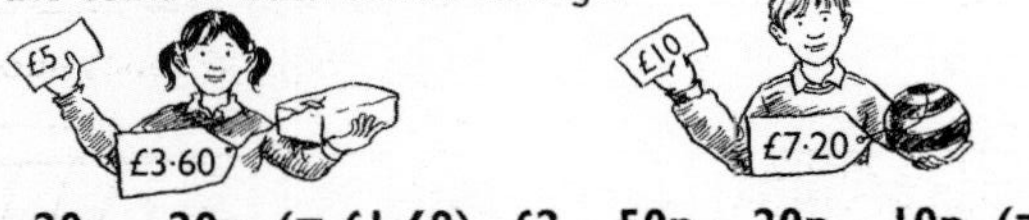

£1, 20p, 20p (= £1.40) £2, 50p, 20p, 10p (= £2.80)

£1·60 — £0·50 — 70p — £1·30

Find the total cost of

pie and chips **£2·90** — ice cream and drink **£1·20**

Money: Textbook pages 65–67

Name: **Check-up 20**

What fraction of each shape is shaded?

$\frac{3}{4}$ — **1**

one half of 28 = **14** — one quarter of 24 = **6**

$\frac{1}{4}$ of 40 = **10** — $\frac{1}{2}$ of 22 = **11**

How many squares are shaded?

3 — **$2\frac{1}{2}$** — **$\frac{1}{4}$** — **$4\frac{1}{4}$**

0 $\frac{1}{2}$ 1 $1\frac{1}{2}$ 2 $2\frac{1}{2}$ 3 $3\frac{1}{2}$ 4 $4\frac{1}{2}$ 5 $5\frac{1}{2}$ 6 $6\frac{1}{2}$ 7

Count in halves. Write each number

- from 0 to 3 **0 $\frac{1}{2}$ 1 $1\frac{1}{2}$ 2 $2\frac{1}{2}$ 3**
- from 5 to 2. **5 $4\frac{1}{2}$ 4 $3\frac{1}{2}$ 3 $2\frac{1}{2}$ 2**

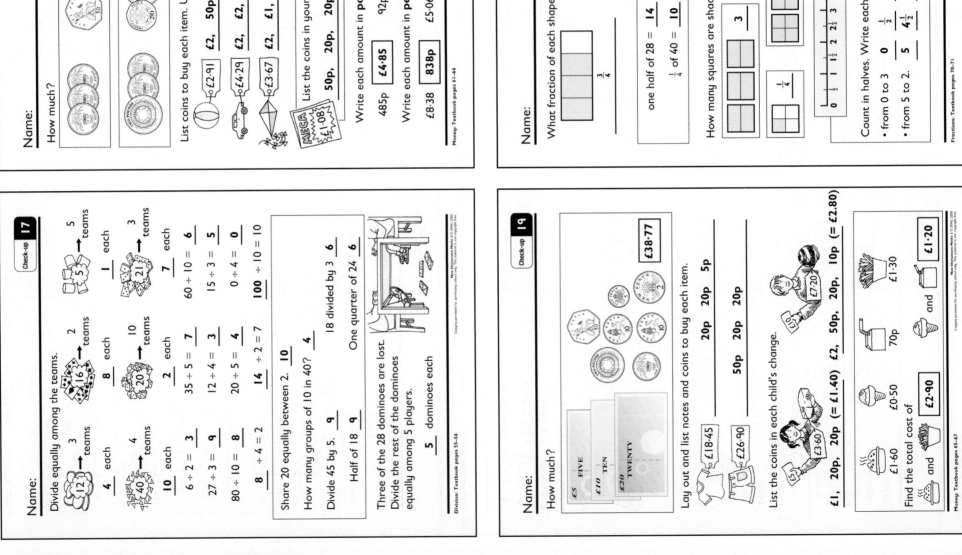

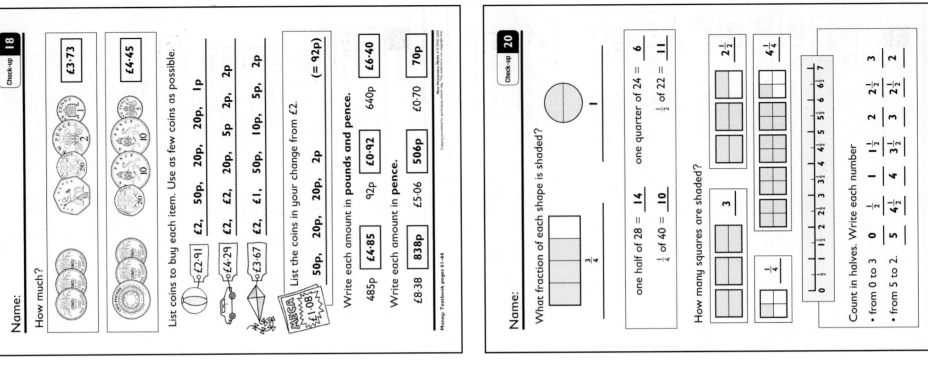

Fractions: Textbook pages 70–71

Name: **Check-up 21**

Colour

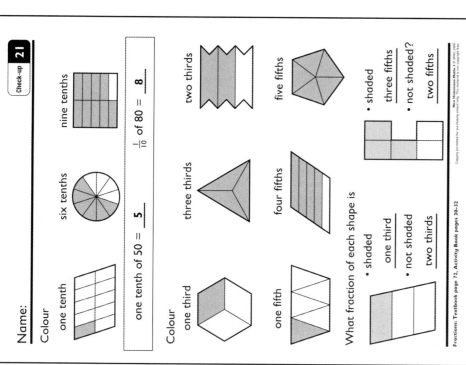

one tenth | six tenths | nine tenths

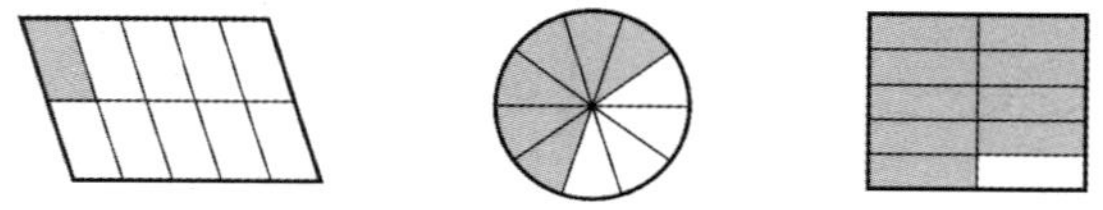

one tenth of 50 = 5 $\frac{1}{10}$ of 80 = 8

Colour

one third | three thirds | two thirds

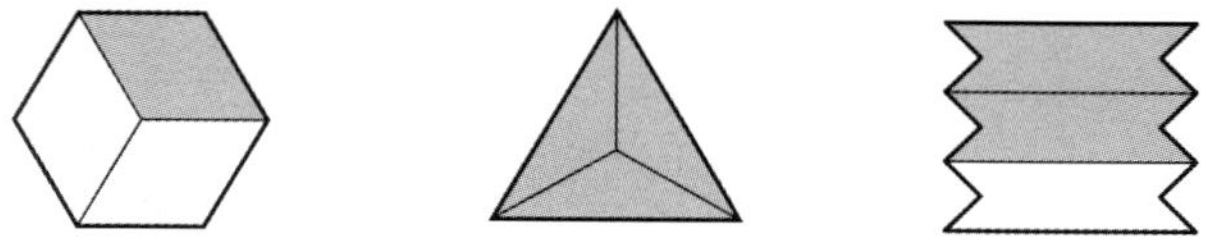

one fifth | four fifths | five fifths

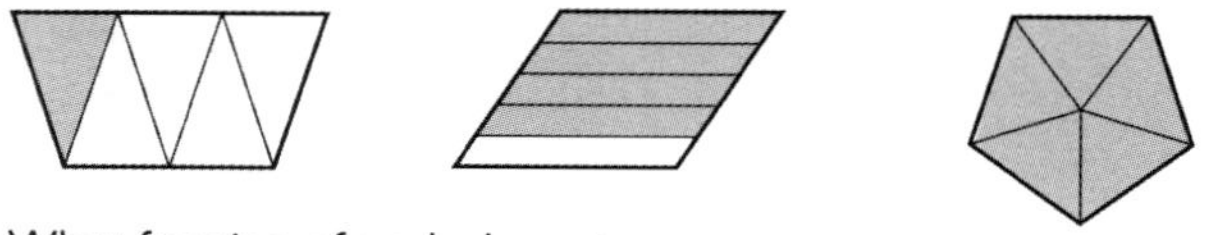

What fraction of each shape is

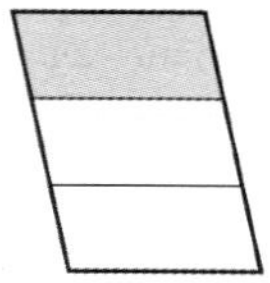

- shaded one third
- not shaded two thirds

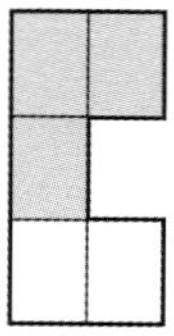

- shaded three fifths
- not shaded? two fifths

Fractions: Textbook page 72, Activity Book pages 30–32

Name: **Check-up 22**

Double each number.

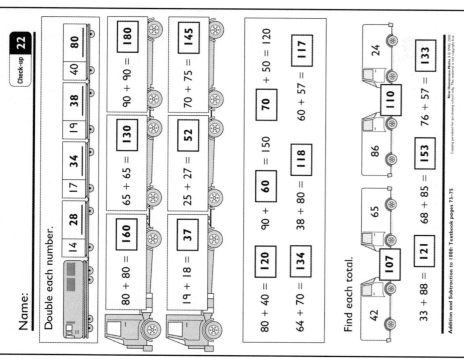

14 **28** | 17 **34** | 19 **38** | 40 **80**

80 + 80 = **160** 65 + 65 = **130** 90 + 90 = **180**

19 + 18 = **37** 25 + 27 = **52** 70 + 75 = **145**

80 + 40 = **120** 90 + **60** = 150 **70** + 50 = 120

64 + 70 = **134** 38 + 80 = **118** 60 + 57 = **117**

Find each total.

42 + 65 → **107** 86 + 24 → **110**

33 + 88 = **121** 68 + 85 = **153** 76 + 57 = **133**

Addition and Subtraction to 1000: Textbook pages 73–75

Name: **Check-up 23**

232 plus 5 = **237** What is the sum of 185 and 7? **192**

546 + 6 = **552** Add 4 to 398. **402**

Add 9.	
183	**192**
615	**624**
494	**503**

Add 11.	
642	**653**
318	**329**
589	**600**

710 + 60 = **770** 30 + 250 = **280**

320 + **80** = 400 **70** + 530 = 600

542 + 40 = **582** 50 + 919 = **969**

Make 1000.

200 + **800** **500** + 500 700 + **300**

300 + 200 = **500** 56 + 400 = **456**

500 + 107 = **607** 638 + 200 = **838**

How many cans were collected altogether by

Cans collected in	Week 1	Week 2
Class 1	43	325
Class 2	56	412

Class 1 **368** Class 2? **468**

Addition and Subtraction to 1000: Textbook pages 76–80

Name: **Check-up 24**

Subtract 10.

405 → **395** 500 → **490** 902 → **892**

161 – 90 = **71** 112 – 40 = **72** 124 – **70** = 54

Take away 9.	
274	**265**
306	**297**
800	**791**

Subtract 11.	
527	**516**
221	**210**
609	**598**

502 – 400 = **102** 759 – 500 = **259**

720 – 500 = 220 837 – **400** = 437

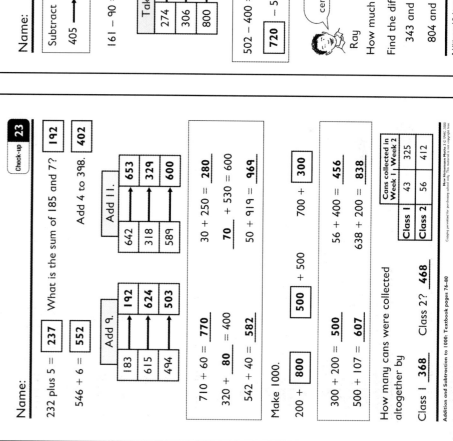

I am 128 centimetres tall.

Ray

I am 135 centimetres tall.

Cara

How much taller is Cara than Ray? **7** centimetres

Find the difference between

343 and 337 **6** 561 and 558 **3**

804 and 799 **5** 695 and 702 **7**

Addition and Subtraction to 1000: Textbook pages 81–84

Assessment

Check-up 25

Name:

Write these times using

o'clock or half past or quarter past or quarter to

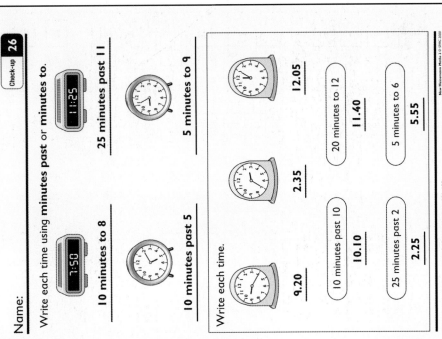

half past nine

11:45
quarter to twelve

quarter past 5

8:00
8 o'clock

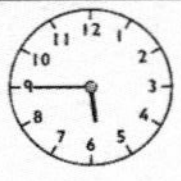
quarter to six

4:15
quarter past 4

Write these times.

Half past one. **1.30**

Quarter to five. **4.45**

 **4.00**

 **12.15**

 **2.45**

Write these times in order starting with the **earliest**.

11.15 pm

Six thirty in the morning.

Quarter to two in the afternoon.

9.00 am

6.30 am **9.00 am** **1.45 pm** **11.15 pm**

Time: Textbook pages 98–100

Check-up 26

Name:

Write each time using **minutes past** or **minutes to**.

10 minutes to 8

25 minutes past 11

10 minutes past 5

5 minutes to 9

Write each time.

 **9.20**

 **2.35**

 **12.05**

10 minutes past 10 **10.10**

20 minutes to 12 **11.40**

25 minutes past 2 **2.25**

5 minutes to 6 **5.55**

Time: Activity Book pages 34–35, Textbook pages 101–102

Check-up 27

Name:

How long?

 → 
45 minutes

 → 
20 minutes

6:10 → 6:45
35 minutes

3:50 → 4:25
35 minutes

 → 
6 hours

11:55 → 3:55
4 hours

start

finish
12:20
35 minutes

Gary left home at 10.05 am.
He returned at 1.05 pm.
How long was he away? **3** hours

Time: Activity Book page 36, Textbook pages 103–104

Topic Assessment 1a — Numbers to 1000

Name:

1 Complete.

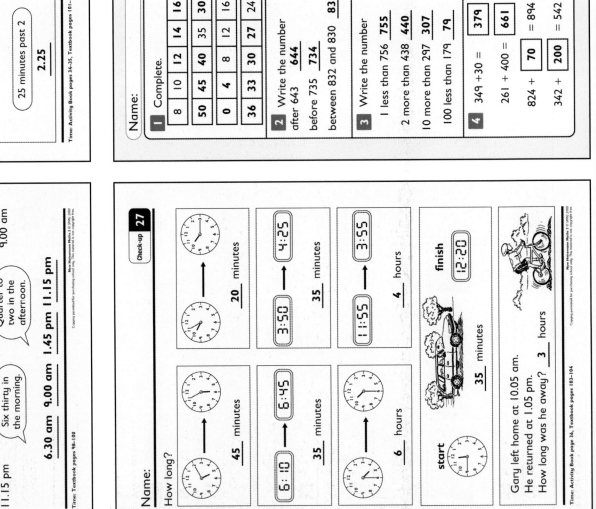

8	10	**12**	**14**	**16**	18	**20**	**22**	24	**26**	**28**
50	**45**	**40**	35	**30**	**25**	20	**15**	**10**	5	0
0	**4**	8	12	16	**20**	**24**	**28**	32	**36**	**40**
36	**33**	**30**	**27**	24	21	18	**15**	**12**	9	**6**

2 Write the number

after 643 **644**

before 735 **734**

between 832 and 830 **831**

after 299 **300**

before 400 **399**

between 599 and 601 **600**

3 Write the number

1 less than 756 **755**

2 more than 438 **440**

10 more than 297 **307**

100 less than 179 **79**

one more than 499 **500**

two less than 501 **499**

ten less than 615 **605**

one hundred more than 900 **1000**

4

349 + 30 = **379**

261 + 400 = **661**

824 + **70** = 894

342 + **200** = 542

673 − 50 = **623**

558 − 500 = **58**

296 − **50** = 246

1000 − **700** = 300

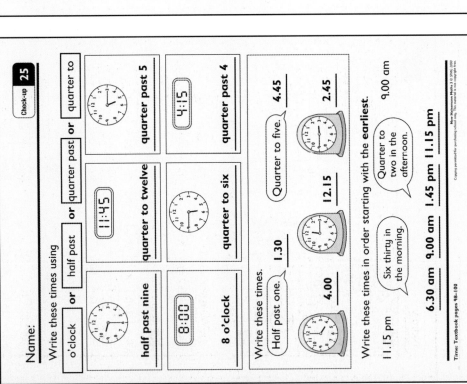

Name:

Topic Assessment — Numbers to 1000 — 1b

1 How many pence?

347 p

2

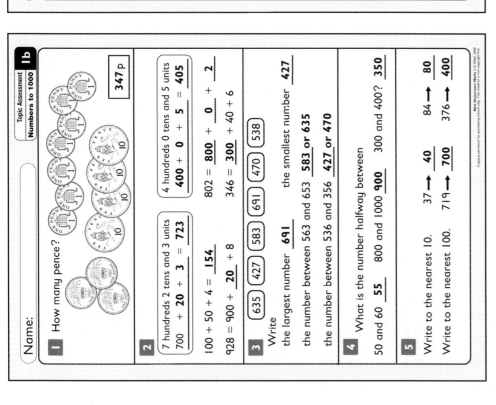

7 hundreds 2 tens and 3 units
700 + **20** + **3** = **723**

4 hundreds 0 tens and 5 units
400 + **0** + **5** = **405**

100 + 50 + 4 = **154**

802 = **800** + **0** + **2**

928 = 900 + **20** + 8

346 = **300** + 40 + 6

3 635 427 583 691 470 538

Write
the largest number **691** the smallest number **427**
the number between 563 and 653 **583 or 635**
the number between 536 and 356 **427 or 470**

4 What is the number halfway between
50 and 60 **55** 800 and 1000 **900** 300 and 400? **350**

5
Write to the nearest 10. 37 → **40** 84 → **80**
Write to the nearest 100. 719 → **700** 376 → **400**

Name:

Topic Assessment — Addition to 100 — 2a

1
12 + 7 = **19** 13 + 5 = **18** 4 + 16 = **20**
3 + **12** = 15 **11** + 9 = 20

2
72 + 4 = **76** 5 + 93 = **98** 41 + 7 = **48**
36 + **3** = 39 **52** + 8 = 60 6 + **21** = 27

3
20 + 60 = **80** 37 + 40 = **77** 50 + 48 = **98**
42 + **30** = 72 **23** + 70 = 93

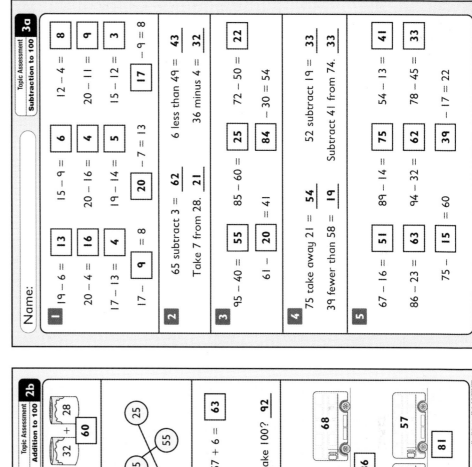

4
35 + 21 = **56** 27 + 51 = **78**
66 + 29 = **95** 44 + 49 = **93**

5
53 + 14 = **67** 17 + 42 = **59** 34 + 15 = **49**

Name:

Topic Assessment — Addition to 100 — 2b

1
44 + 52 = **96** 75 + 23 = **98** 32 + 28 = **60**

2 Match pairs which add to make 100.
5 — 95, 65 — 35, 15 — 85, 45 — 55, 75 — 25

3
15 + 7 = **22** 4 + 88 = **92** 57 + 6 = **63**

What must be added
to 36 to make 44 **8** to 8 to make 100? **92**

4 Find each total.
13 + 37 = **50** 18 + 68 = **86**
45 + 38 = **83** 24 + 57 = **81**

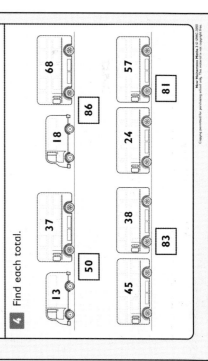

Name:

Topic Assessment — Subtraction to 100 — 3a

1
19 – 6 = **13** 15 – 9 = **6** 12 – 4 = **8**
20 – 4 = **16** 20 – 16 = **4** 20 – 11 = **9**
17 – 13 = **4** 19 – 14 = **5** 15 – 12 = **3**
17 – **9** = 8 **20** – 7 = 13 **17** – 9 = 8

2
65 subtract 3 = **62** 6 less than 49 = **43**
Take 7 from 28. **21** 36 minus 4 = **32**

3
95 – 40 = **55** 85 – 60 = **25** 72 – 50 = **22**
61 – **20** = 41 **84** – 30 = 54

4
75 take away 21 = **54** 52 subtract 19 = **33**
39 fewer than 58 = **19** Subtract 41 from 74. **33**

5
67 – 16 = **51** 89 – 14 = **75** 54 – 13 = **41**
86 – 23 = **63** 94 – 32 = **62** 78 – 45 = **33**
75 – **15** = 60 **39** – 17 = 22

Assessment

Topic Assessment 3b — Subtraction to 100

Name:

1
28 – 9 = **19**   23 – 7 = **16**   26 – **8** = 18
83 – 6 = **77**   71 – 4 = **67**   44 – **7** = 37

2
32 – 15 = **17**   46 – 18 = **28**   28 – 13 **15**
58 – **19** = 39   **76** – 14 = 62

3
86
Give away 27.
How many are left? **59**
72 – 35 = **37**
64 – 28 = **36**

4 Complete the number stories.

8 17 25
8 + 17 = **25**
17 + 8 = **25**
25 – 8 = **17**
25 – 17 = **8**

32 47 15
32 + 15 = **47**
15 + **32** = 47
47 – **32** = 15
47 – 15 = **32**

Topic Assessment 4a — Multiplication

Name:

1 Multiply.
10 × 7 = **70**   2 × 9 = **18**   10 × 6 = **60**
8 × 2 = **16**   8 × 10 = **80**   7 × 2 = **14**
10 × 9 = **90**   2 × 6 = **12**   10 × 10 = **100**

2
5 × 5 = **25**   7 × 5 = **35**   5 × 9 = **45**
6 × 5 = **30**   5 × 4 = **20**   5 × 8 = **40**

3
Sand £7   Soil £10   Grit £3
What is the cost of 3 sacks of
Sand **£21**   Soil **£30**   Grit? **£9**
3 × 9 = **27**   3 × 6 = **18**   3 × 0 = **0**

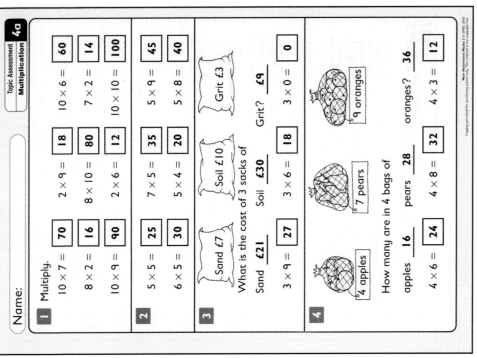

4
4 apples   7 pears   9 oranges
How many are in 4 bags of
apples **16**   pears **28**   oranges? **36**
4 × 6 = **24**   4 × 8 = **32**   4 × 3 = **12**

Topic Assessment 4b — Multiplication

Name:

1 Match.
4 times 5   2 × 6   5 times 2   4 × 10
12   20   40   10
3 times 4   8 × 5   10 times 1   10 × 2

2
3 × **5** = 15   4 × **0** = 0   10 × **3** = 30
4 × 2 = 8   **9** × 4 = 36   **8** × 3 = 24

3 Cross (×)
multiples of 50: 255 ~~150~~ 210 ~~50~~ ~~300~~ 505 ~~400~~
multiples of 100.: 270 ~~600~~ 305 ~~500~~ 80 ~~700~~ ~~100~~

4
3 × 20 = **60**   5 × 30 = **150**   10 × 50 = **500**
40 × 4 = **160**   2 × 45 = **90**   40 × 5 = **200**
3 × 31 = **93**   4 × 22 = **88**   3 × 23 = **69**

Topic Assessment 5a — Division

Name:

1
6 ÷ 2 = **3**   90 ÷ 10 = **9**   16 ÷ 2 = **8**
50 ÷ 10 = **5**   20 ÷ 2 = **10**   100 ÷ 10 = **10**
Half of 8 = **4**   40 divided by 10 = **4**
$\frac{1}{2}$ of 18 = **9**   Divide 70 by 10. **7**

2 Share equally among 5 boxes.
25 **5**   40 **8**   15 **3**
20 ÷ 5 = 4   **45** ÷ 5 = 9   **0** ÷ 5 = 0

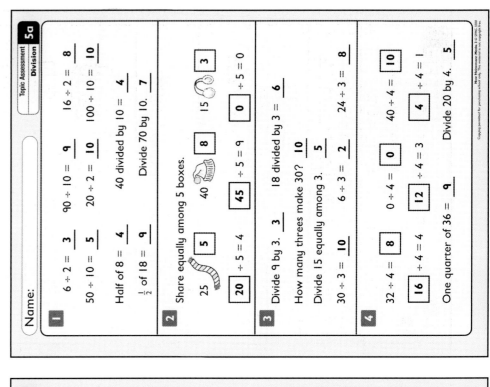

3
Divide 9 by 3. **3**   18 divided by 3 = **6**
How many threes make 30? **10**
Divide 15 equally among 3. **5**
30 ÷ 3 = **10**   6 ÷ 3 = **2**   24 ÷ 3 = **8**

4
32 ÷ 4 = **8**   0 ÷ 4 = **0**   40 ÷ 4 = **10**
16 ÷ 4 = 4   **12** ÷ 4 = 3   **4** ÷ 4 = 1
One quarter of 36 = **9**   Divide 20 by 4. **5**

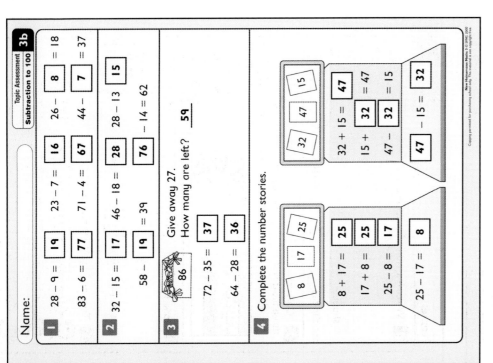

Name:

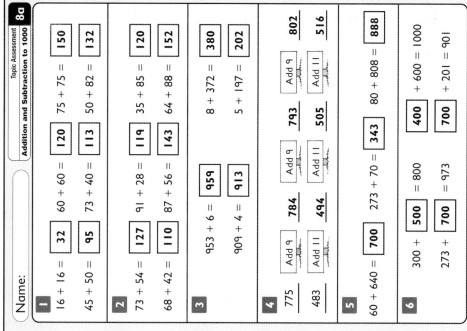

Topic Assessment **5b** Division

1 There are 24 bottles in the crate.
Half of them are green.
One quarter of the green bottles are empty.
How many green bottles are empty? **3**

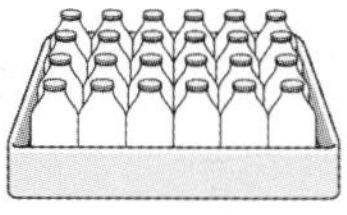

2

15 multiplied by 2 **30** half of 30 **15**

double 300 **600** half of 600 **300**

800 divided by 2 **400** twice 500 **1000**

700 ÷ 100 = **7** 700 ÷ 10 = **70**

600 ÷ 10 = **60** 1000 ÷ 100 = **10**

3 5 × 4 = 20 Write two division stories.

20 ÷ 4 = 5 **20 ÷ 5 = 4**

4 Match.

Divide me by 5 and my remainder is 2. — 17

16 18 17

Divide me by 3 and my remainder is 1. — 16

5 A box holds 3 dice. How many boxes are needed for 29 dice? **10**

Name:

Topic Assessment **6** Money

1 Write in pence £3·84 **384p**

in pounds and pence. 705p **£7·05**

2 List coins in your change from £2 when you buy

73p **£1, 20p, 5p and 2p (= £1·27)**

3 How much?

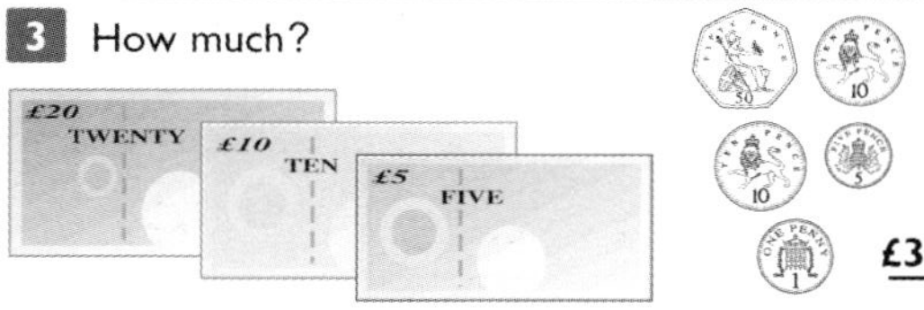

£35.76

4

I had £10.
I spent £3·60.
How much have I left?

£6.40

5

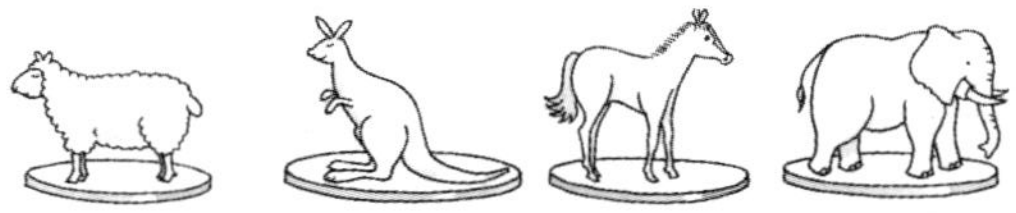

£0·80 £1·40 90p £2·20

What is the total cost of the elephant and kangaroo **£3·60** sheep and horse? **£1·70**

Name:

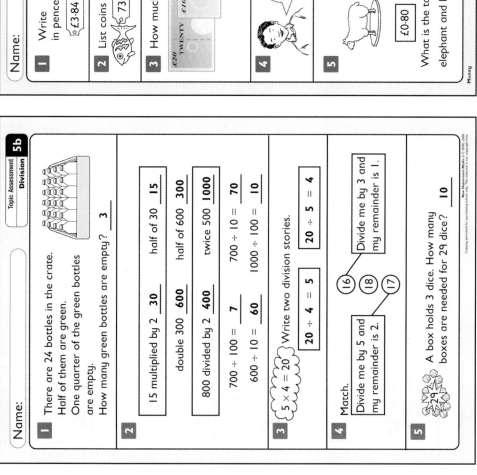

Topic Assessment **7** Fractions

1 What fraction of each shape is

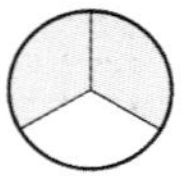

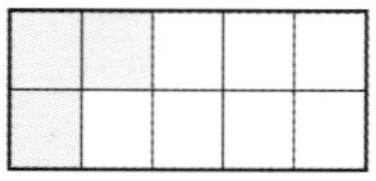

shaded $\frac{2}{3}$ shaded $\frac{3}{10}$

not shaded $\frac{1}{3}$ not shaded? $\frac{7}{10}$

2 Colour

three fifths red one fifth green

one half red one quarter green

five tenths red one half green.

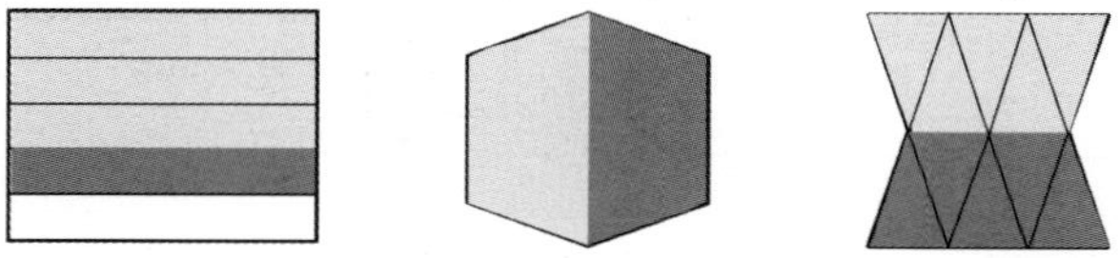

3 one half of 30 = **15** $\frac{1}{10}$ of 30 = **3**

$\frac{1}{4}$ of 36 = **9** $\frac{1}{2}$ of 24 = **12**

one tenth of 100 = **10** one quarter of 28 = **7**

4 True or False? Tick (✓) the box.

One quarter is greater than one half. T F ✓

One half is less than three quarters. T ✓ F

One half is the same as two quarters. T ✓ F

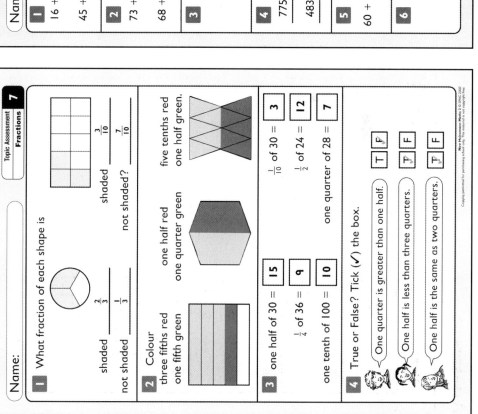

Name:

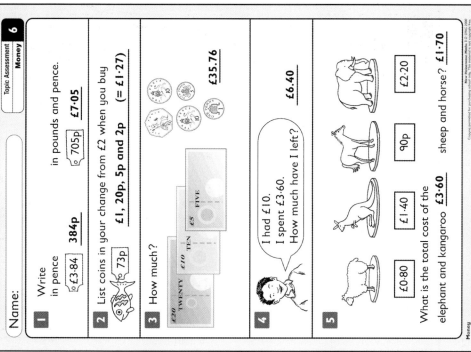

Topic Assessment **8a** Addition and Subtraction to 1000

1

16 + 16 = **32** 60 + 60 = **120** 75 + 75 = **150**

45 + 50 = **95** 73 + 40 = **113** 50 + 82 = **132**

2

73 + 54 = **127** 91 + 28 = **119** 35 + 85 = **120**

68 + 42 = **110** 87 + 56 = **143** 64 + 88 = **152**

3

953 + 6 = **959** 8 + 372 = **380**

909 + 4 = **913** 5 + 197 = **202**

4

775 Add 9 **784** Add 9 **793** Add 9 **802**

483 Add 11 **494** Add 11 **505** Add 11 **516**

5

60 + 640 = **700** 273 + 70 = **343** 80 + 808 = **888**

6

300 + **500** = 800 **400** + 600 = 1000

273 + **700** = 973 **700** + 201 = 901

Name:

Topic Assessment
Addition and Subtraction to 1000 **8b**

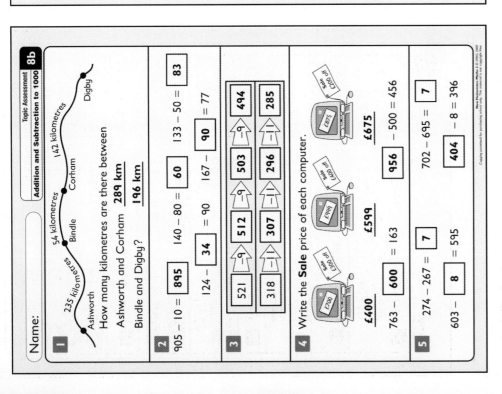

1

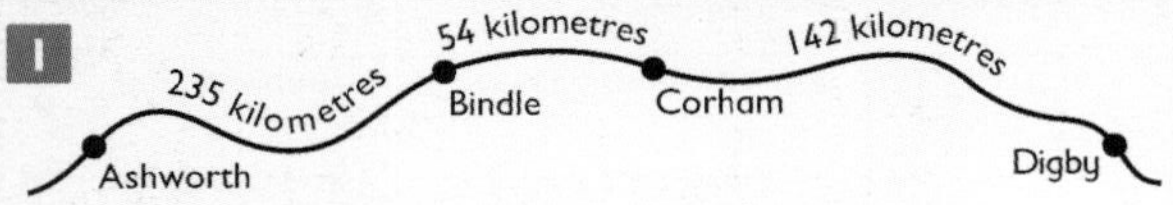

How many kilometres are there between

Ashworth and Corham **289 km**

Bindle and Digby? **196 km**

2

905 – 10 = **895** 140 – 80 = **60** 133 – 50 = **83**

124 – **34** = 90 167 – **90** = 77

3

521 → –9 → **512** → –9 → **503** → –9 → **494**

318 → –11 → **307** → –11 → **296** → –11 → **285**

4 Write the **Sale** price of each computer.

£400 **£599** **£675**

763 – **600** = 163 **956** – 500 = 456

5

274 – 267 = **7** 702 – 695 = **7**

603 – **8** = 595 **404** – 8 = 396

Name:

Topic Assessment
Time **9a**

1 Write each time using

o'clock **or** half past **or** quarter past **or** quarter to.

quarter to 7 **half past 3**

quarter past 2 **ten o'clock**

2 Write these times using am or pm.

Quarter past seven in the morning. **7.15 am**

Half past three in the afternoon. **3.30 pm**

3 Write each time using **minutes past** or **minutes to**.

25 minutes past 2 **5 minutes to 9**

Name:

Topic Assessment
Time **9b**

1 Write each time.

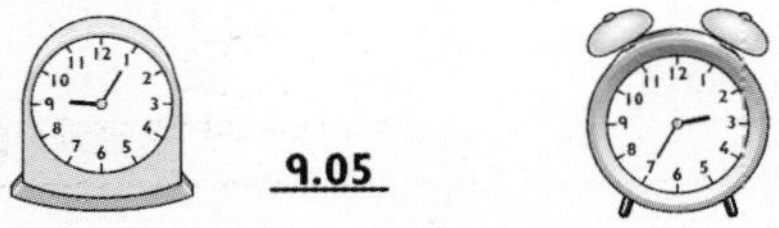

9.05 **2.35**

20 minutes to 5 **4.40** quarter past 11 **11.15**

2 Write in order, starting with the **earliest**.

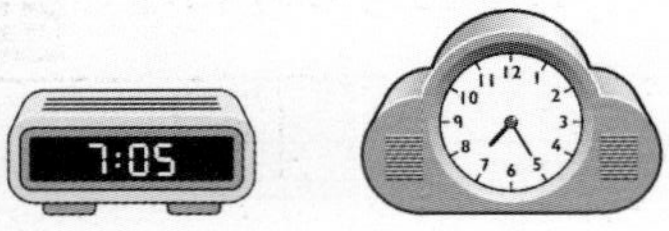

Ten minutes to seven.

6.50 **7.05** **7.25**

3 How long?

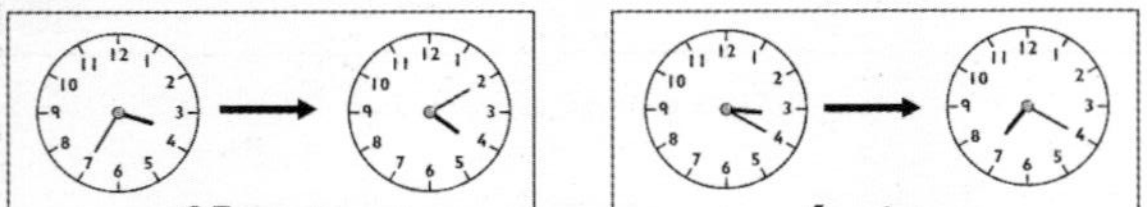

95 minutes **4** hours

9:15 → 9:40 **25** minutes

11:25 → 12:10 **45** minutes

Name:

Round-up **1**

1 Write the missing numbers.

183	**193**	**203**	213	223	233	**243**
78	**178**	**278**	**378**	478	578	678

2 Write the number

after 609 **610** before 212 **211**

3

215 + 10 = **225** 668 – 40 = **628**

4

15 + 4 = **19** 11 + 7 = **18** 12 + 6 = **18**

14 + **4** = 18 **13** + 2 = 15

5 Make each price 4p more.

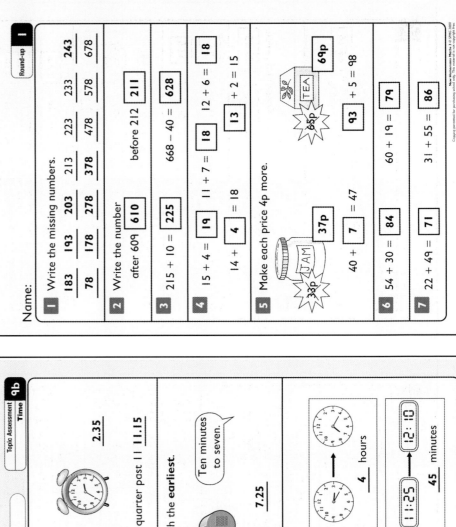

37p

69p

40 + **7** = 47 **93** + 5 = 98

6

54 + 30 = **84** 60 + 19 = **79**

7

22 + 49 = **71** 31 + 55 = **86**

Name: Round-up 1

8 Subtract 6 from 14. **8** Take 8 from 13. **5**

12 – 5 = **7** 17 – 8 = **9**

18 – 13 = **5** 20 – 12 = **8**

20 – **17** = 3 15 – **7** = 8

9 Subtract 4. 67 **63** Subtract 7. 49 **42** Subtract 3. 78 **75**

10 Take 40 from 73. **33** 59 – 30 = **29**

Subtract 20 from 62. **42** 88 – 40 = **48**

11 81 – 59 = **22** 65 – 31 = **34**

12 How many groups of 5? 35 **7** 20 **4**

13 40 ÷ 5 = **8** 25 ÷ 5 = **5** 0 ÷ 5 = **0**

Name: Round-up 1

14 How much?

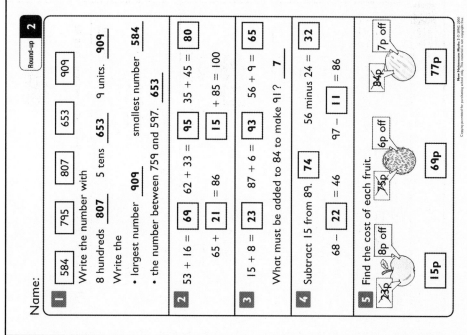

£4·36

15 Write

- in pence £3·08 **308p**
- in pounds and pence. 645p **£6·45**

16 19 + 19 = **38** 16 + 18 = **34**

35 + 35 = **70** 80 + 75 = **155**

17 How much altogether? 42 73 **115** 68 56 **124**

18 483 + 8 = **491** 7 + 116 = **123**

19 265 + 9 = **274** 424 + 11 = **435**

Name: Round-up 1

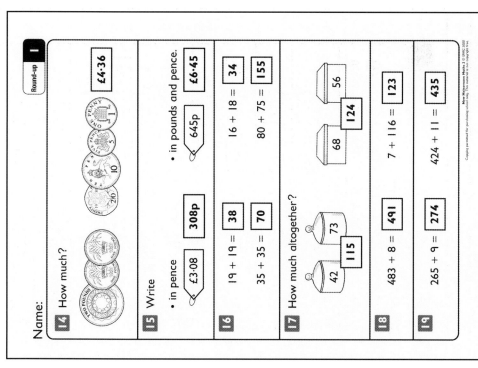

20 Colour **two** items which together weigh 1 kg.

400g 500g 300g 600g

21 Write the length of each object.

9 cm **$10\frac{1}{2}$ cm**

22 Write these times using o'clock **or** half past **or** quarter past **or** quarter to.

quarter to 8 **half past 3** **4 o'clock**

23 Write the position of

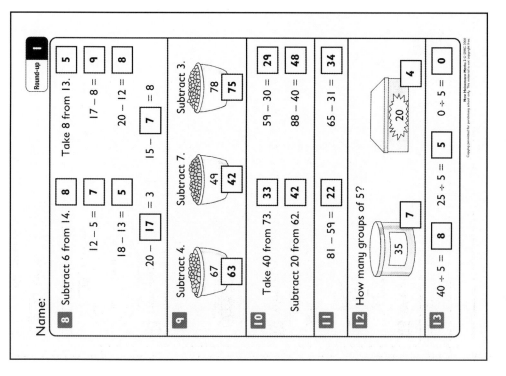

C2

B1

D3

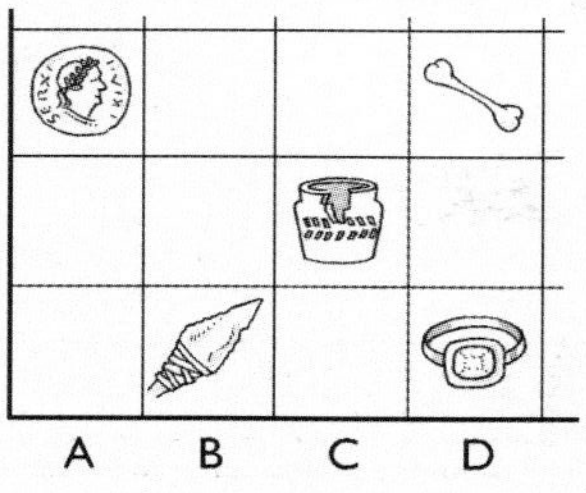

Name: Round-up 2

1 584 795 807 653 909

Write the number with

8 hundreds **807** 5 tens **653** 9 units. **909**

Write the

- largest number **909** smallest number **584**
- the number between 759 and 597. **653**

2 53 + 16 = **69** 62 + 33 = **95** 35 + 45 = **80**

65 + **21** = 86 **15** + 85 = 100

3 15 + 8 = **23** 87 + 6 = **93** 56 + 9 = **65**

What must be added to 84 to make 91? **7**

4 Subtract 15 from 89. **74** 56 minus 24 = **32**

68 – **22** = 46 97 – **11** = 86

5 Find the cost of each fruit.

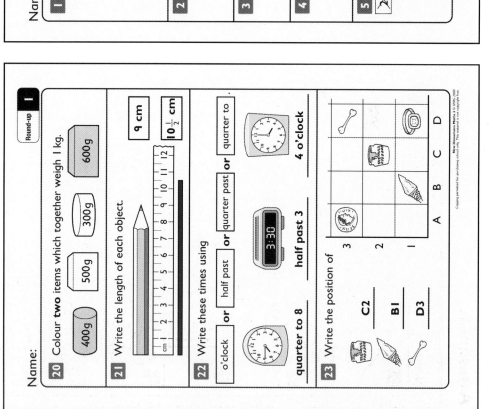

~~23p~~ 8p off **15p** ~~75p~~ 6p off **69p** ~~84p~~ 7p off **77p**

Name: Round-up 2

6 3 × 9 = **27** 8 × 4 = **32** 4 × 3 = **12**

7 multiplied by 4. **28** Multiply 6 by 3. **18**

4 × **5** = 20 3 × **0** = 0 4 × **9** = 36

7 12 ÷ 4 = **3** 21 ÷ 3 = **7** 40 ÷ 4 = **10**

Divide 27 by 3. **9** 20 divided by 4 **5**

30 ÷ 3 = 10 **16** ÷ 4 = 4 **15** ÷ 3 = 5

8 List the coins in your change from £1.

58p **20p, 20p, 2p**

List the coins in your change from £2.

£1·33 **50p, 10p, 5p, 2p**

9

One tenth of the apples are red.

How many apples are red? **3**

one tenth of 70 = **7** $\frac{1}{10}$ of 90 = **9**

10 240 + 50 = **290** 50 + 550 = **600**

500 + 194 = **694** 86 + 700 = **786**

823 + 65 = **888** 205 + 94 = **299**

Name: Round-up 2

11 765 – 20 = **745** 899 – 50 = **849**

145 – **50** = 95 130 – **70** = 60

12 Find the area of each shape in squares.

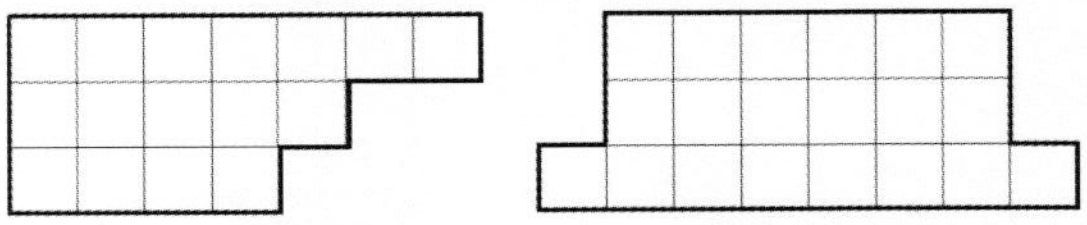

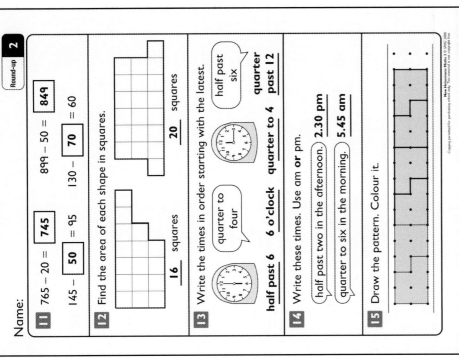

16 squares **20** squares

13 Write the times in order starting with the latest.

(quarter to four)  (half past six)

half past 6 **6 o'clock** **quarter to 4** **quarter past 12**

14 Write these times. Use am **or** pm.

half past two in the afternoon. **2.30 pm**

quarter to six in the morning. **5.45 am**

15 Draw the pattern. Colour it.

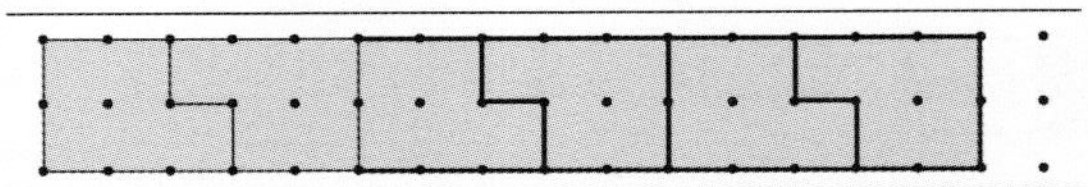

Name: Round-up 2

16 Use a right angle tester.
How many right angles in each shape?

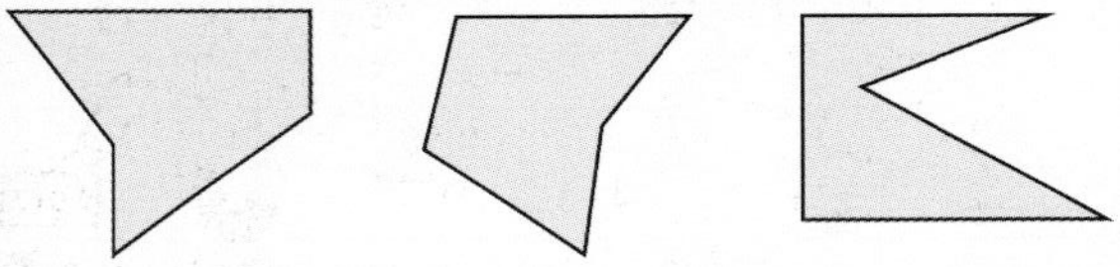

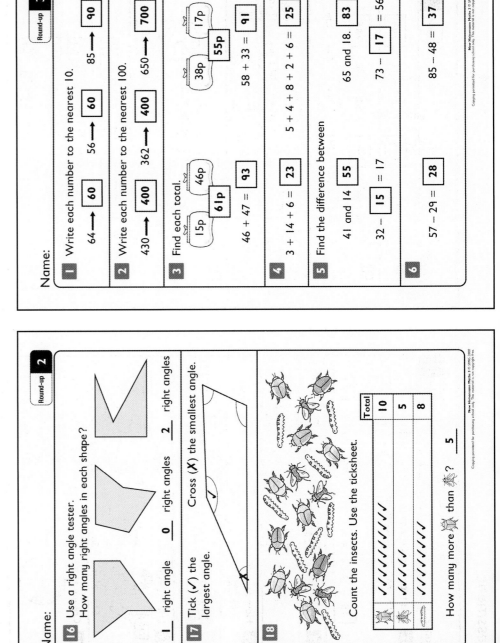

1 right angle **0** right angles **2** right angles

17 Tick (✓) the largest angle. Cross (✗) the smallest angle.

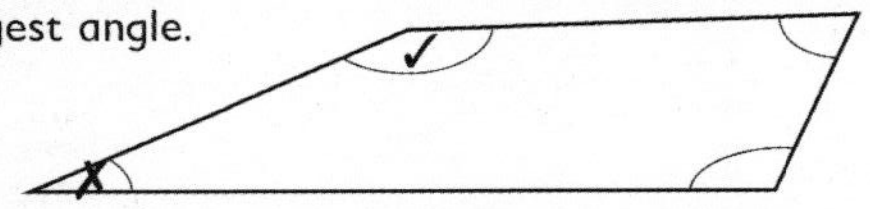

18

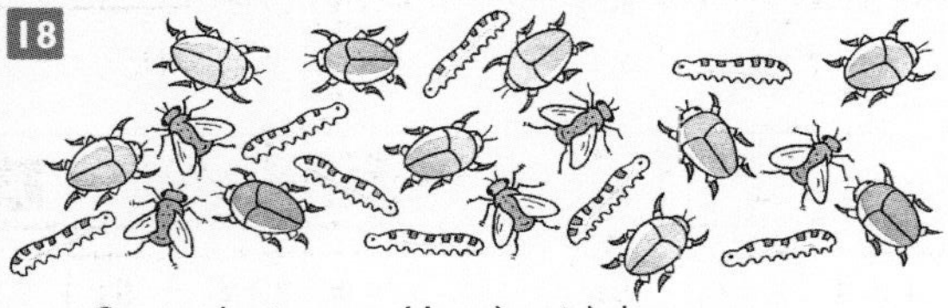

Count the insects. Use the ticksheet.

		Total
beetle	✓✓✓✓✓✓✓✓✓✓	10
fly	✓✓✓✓✓	5
caterpillar	✓✓✓✓✓✓✓✓	8

How many more beetles than flies? **5**

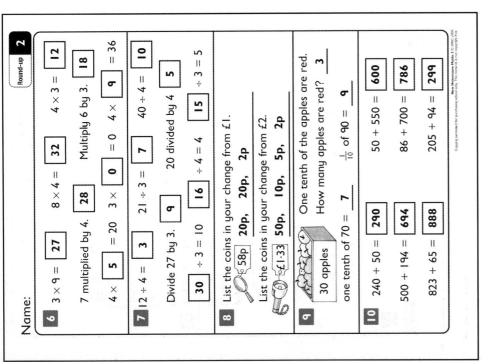

Name: Round-up 3

1 Write each number to the nearest 10.

64 → **60** 56 → **60** 85 → **90**

2 Write each number to the nearest 100.

430 → **400** 362 → **400** 650 → **700**

3 Find each total.

15p 46p **61p** 38p 17p **55p**

46 + 47 = **93** 58 + 33 = **91**

4 3 + 14 + 6 = **23** 5 + 4 + 8 + 2 + 6 = **25**

5 Find the difference between

41 and 14 **55** 65 and 18. **83**

32 – **15** = 17 73 – **17** = 56

6 57 – 29 = **28** 85 – 48 = **37**

Name: Round-up 3

7 Use the multiplication fact.
Write two division stories.

5 × 3 = 15

15 ÷ 3 = 5   15 ÷ 5 = 3

8

40 × 3 = **120**   4 × 20 = **80**

31 × 2 = **62**   3 × 22 = **66**

9 How much?

£36·53

10 List the coins in each child's change.

£2, 50p, 20p   **£2, £1, 20p, 5p**

11 Colour one third.   Colour four fifths.

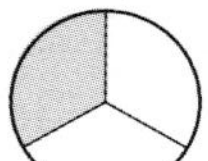

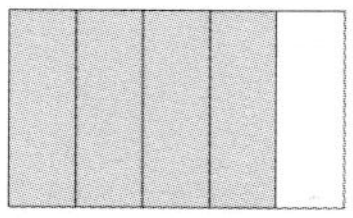

New Heinemann Maths 3 © SPMG 2000
Copying permitted for purchasing school only. This material is not copyright free.

Name: Round-up 3

12

673 − 9 = **664**   219 − 11 = **208**

13

800 − 600 = **200**   585 − 300 = **285**

579 − 100 = 479   **706** − 400 = 306

14 What is the difference in height between the

Elm and Ash **4 cm**

Ash and Oak? **5 cm**

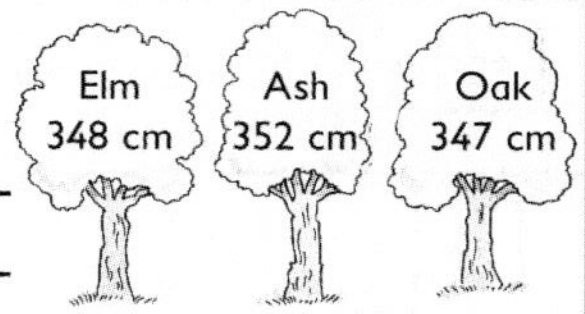

15 Write each time.

quarter to 5

2.25   **4.45**   **6.50**

16 Colour to make the pattern symmetrical.

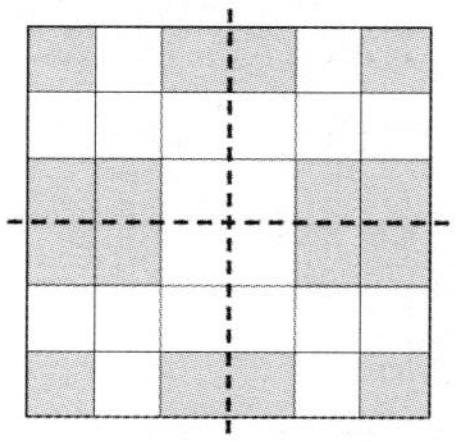

New Heinemann Maths 3 © SPMG 2000
Copying permitted for purchasing school only. This material is not copyright free.

Name: Round-up 3

17

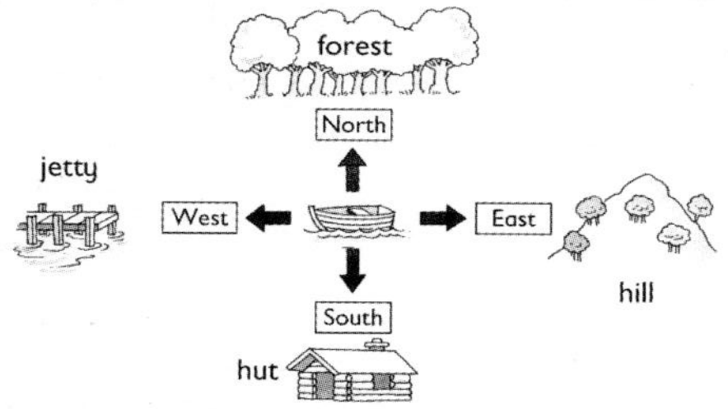

You are in the boat.
What do you see when you look south? **hut**

Face East.
In which direction are you facing when you turn 3 right angles anti-clockwise? **South**

18 These are class 3's favourite flowers.

daisy	4
tulip	7
rose	5
pansy	2

Complete the barchart.

Class 3's favourite flowers

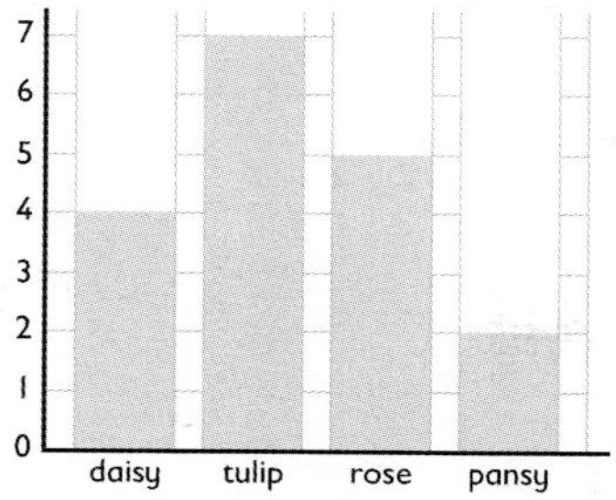

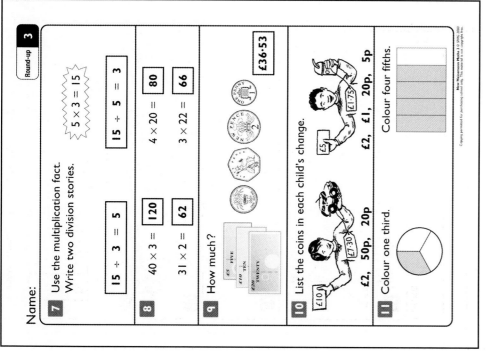

Published by Heinemann Educational Publishers, Halley Court, Jordan Hill, Oxford OX2 8EJ,
a division of Reed Educational and Professional Publishing Ltd.
ISBN 0 435 17209 3 © Scottish Primary Mathematics Group 2000.
First published 2000. 04 03 02 01 00 10 9 8 7 6 5 4 3 2 1
Designed and illustrated by Gecko Ltd. Printed by Pindar plc, Scarborough.
ISBN 0-435-17209-3

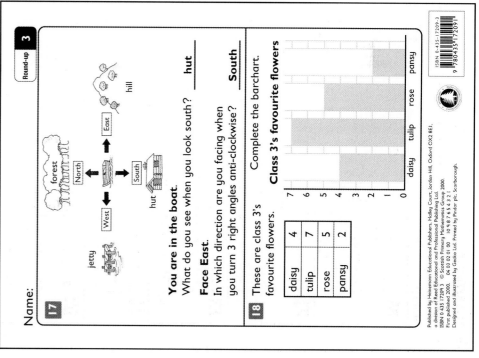

HOME ACTIVITY 1

What is my hat number?

My number is
- between 600 and 700
- less than 640.

My number is
- between 630 and 660
- greater than 640.

My number is **609**.

My number is **649**.

Choose one of the other hat numbers.
Write a clue for it.

My number is

Children's answers will vary.

My number is

Write the number

after 283 **284**

before 400 **399**

one more than 693 **694**

one less than 900. **899**

Write **two** numbers between 810 and 825. ____ ____
any 2 from 811 to 824

HOME ACTIVITY 2

186 + 10 = **196**

342 + 30 = **372**

726 + 50 = **776**

962 – 10 = **952**

857 – 20 = **837**

590 – 60 = **530**

216 add 100 **316**

800 subtract 100 **700**

382 add 300 **682**

650 minus 400 **250**

Help The child can count on or count back in 10s or 100s, using fingers, if necessary, to keep track.

HOME ACTIVITY 3

471 322 654 368 259 437

Write

the largest number **654**

the smallest number **259**

the number between 368 and 471 **437**

the number between 368 and 259. **322**

Write the numbers in order. Start with the largest.

654 **471** **437** **368** **322** **259**

HOME ACTIVITY 4

8 + 7 = **15**   5 + 6 = **11**   3 + 8 = **11**

5 + 10 = **15**   6 + 9 = **15**   7 + 4 = **11**

Make 13.

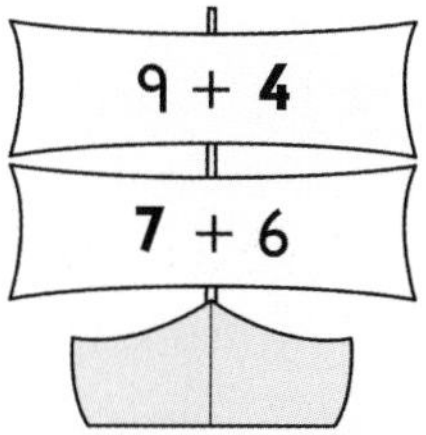

Make 17.

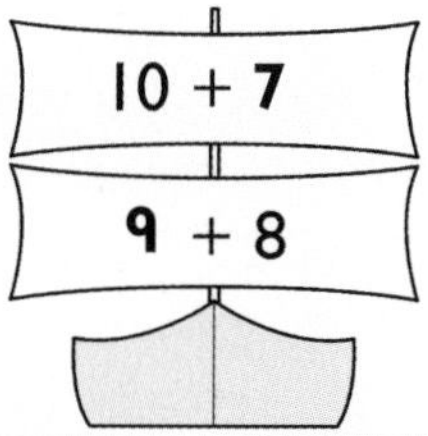

HOME ACTIVITY 5

5 + 14 = **19**   8 + 11 = **19**   16 + 3 = **19**

17 + 2 = **19**   15 + 4 = **19**   6 + 12 = **18**

Make 20.

43 + 5 = **48**   4 + 64 = **68**   52 + 7 = **59**

31 + 6 = **37**   7 + 23 = **30**   85 + 4 = **89**

HOME ACTIVITY 6

37 + 9 = **46**   28 + 19 = **47**   44 + 39 = **83**

56 + 11 = **67**   33 + 21 = **54**   27 + 51 = **78**

29 + 35 = **64**   44 + 31 = **75**   19 + 21 = **40**

HOME ACTIVITY 7

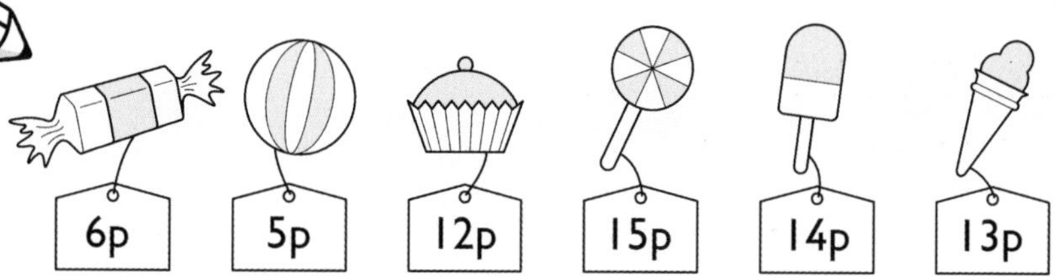

Find the total cost of:

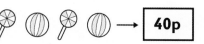

 → **25p**

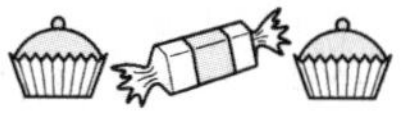 → **30p**

 → **40p**

 → **45p**

HOME ACTIVITY **8**

Subtract 10 from 14. **4**

Take 17 from 19. **2**

13 fewer than 16 **3**

14 less than 20 **6**

15 minus 9 **6**

18 subtract 11 **7**

17 take away 12 **5**

20 minus 15 **5**

Find the difference in price between

 and  £ **8** 

 and  £ **4** 

 and  £ **4** 

HOME ACTIVITY **9**

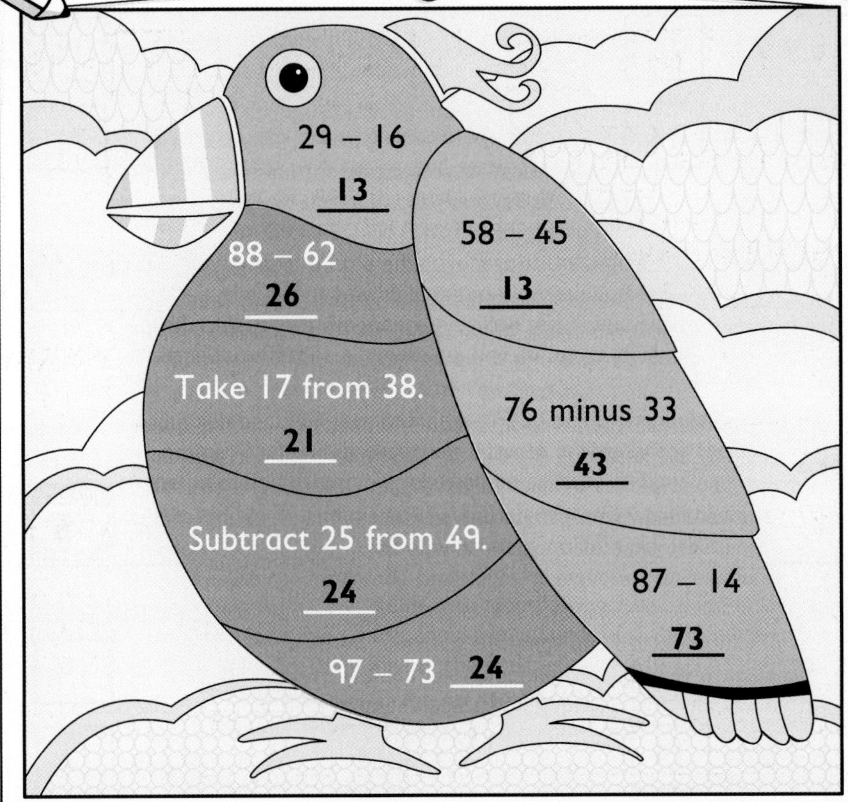

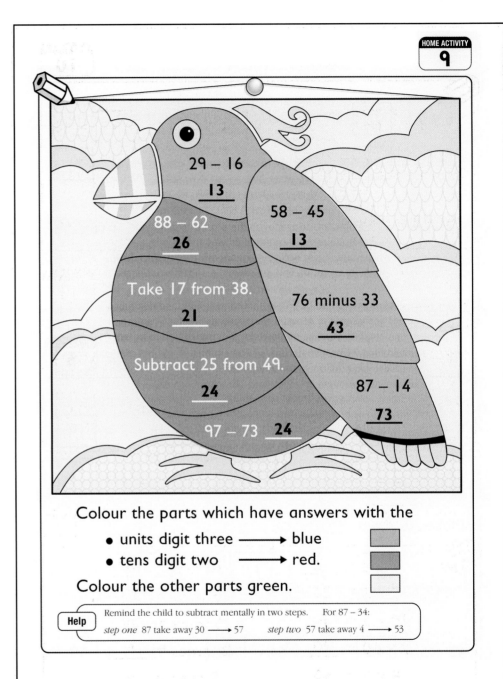

Colour the parts which have answers with the

- units digit three ⟶ blue
- tens digit two ⟶ red.

Colour the other parts green.

Help Remind the child to subtract mentally in two steps. For 87 – 34:
step one 87 take away 30 ⟶ 57 *step two* 57 take away 4 ⟶ 53

HOME ACTIVITY 10

21 – 3 = **18**	22 – 9 = **13**	23 – **7** = 16
25 minus 6 = **19**		Subtract 8 from 24. **16**
91 – 2 = **89**	30 – 4 = **26**	53 – **7** = 46

HOME ACTIVITY 11

42 – 13 = **29**	87 – 18 = **69**	95 – 17 = **78**
31 take away 15 = **16**		70 subtract 16 = **54**
63 – **14** = 49	46 – **18** = 28	**55** – 16 = 39

HOME ACTIVITY 12

2 × 8 = **16**	10 tens = **100**
5 × 5 = **25**	5 twos = **10**
10 × 3 = **30**	5 fours = **20**
2 × 10 = **20**	2 threes = **6**
8 × 5 = **40**	5 ones = **5**
5 × 0 = **0**	5 tens = **50**

HOME ACTIVITY 13

Match.

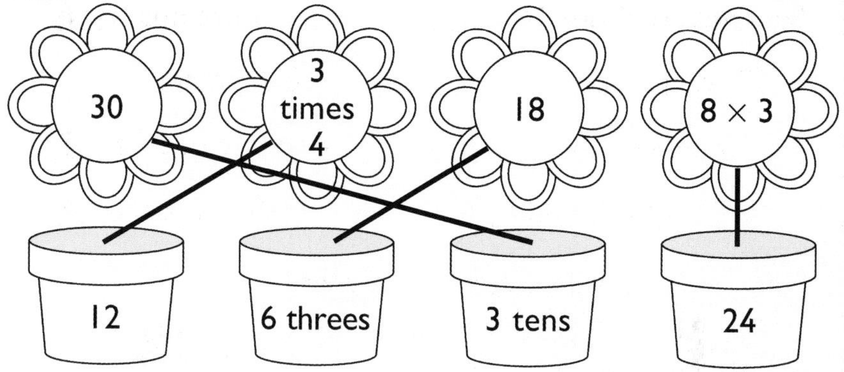

3 × **5** = 15	**0** × 3 = 0
3 × **7** = 21	**2** × 3 = 6
3 × **1** = 3	**9** × 3 = 27

HOME ACTIVITY 14

Mark each example ✓ or ✗.

4 X 9 = 36 ✓	4 X 8 = 32 ✓	4 X 1 = 1 ✗
4 X 6 = 24 ✓	4 X 0 = 4 ✗	4 X 7 = 28 ✓
4 X 10 = 30 ✗	4 X 2 = 8 ✓	4 X 3 = 12 ✓

HOME ACTIVITY **15**

Find the answers. Colour them on the grid below to read the alien's message.

$3 \times 6 =$ **18** $5 \times 5 =$ **25**

$10 \times 2 =$ **20** $4 \times 8 =$ **32**

$9 \times 3 =$ **27** $10 \times 4 =$ **40** $4 \times 4 =$ **16**

$3 \times 7 =$ **21** $4 \times 9 =$ **36** $4 \times 3 =$ **12**

$5 \times 3 =$ **15** $4 \times 7 =$ **28** $3 \times 10 =$ **30**

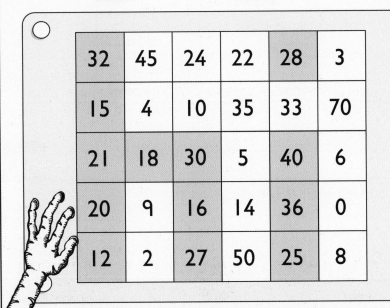

32	45	24	22	28	3
15	4	10	35	33	70
21	18	30	5	40	6
20	9	16	14	36	0
12	2	27	50	25	8

HOME ACTIVITY **16**

Find the cost of:

2  **24p**

2  **70p**

2  **46p**

3  **69p**

3  **36p**

4  **48p**

HOME ACTIVITY **17**

$14 \div 2 =$ **7** $6 \div 2 =$ **3** $18 \div 2 =$ **9**

$90 \div 10 =$ **9** $50 \div 10 =$ **5** $10 \div 10 =$ **1**

half of 4 = **2** half of 60 = **30**

How many twos make 12? **6**

How many tens make 70? **7**

HOME ACTIVITY **18**

Divide.

25 ÷ 5 **5**

50 ÷ 5 **10**

10 ÷ 5 **2**

0 ÷ 5 **0**

20 ÷ 5 **4**

40 ÷ 5 **8**

5 ÷ 5 **1**

35 ÷ 5 **7**

Help Allow the child to jump back in fives on the number line.

0 5 10 15 20 25 30 35 40 45 50

Divide 45 by 5. **9**

15 divided by 5 = **3**

How many fives make 30? **6**

Share 50 equally among 5. **10**

How many groups of five make 25? **5**

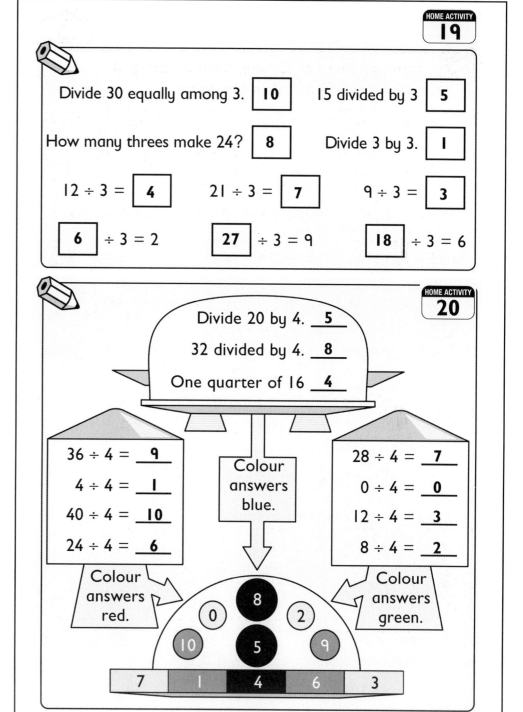

HOME ACTIVITY **19**

Divide 30 equally among 3. **10**

15 divided by 3 **5**

How many threes make 24? **8**

Divide 3 by 3. **1**

12 ÷ 3 = **4**

21 ÷ 3 = **7**

9 ÷ 3 = **3**

6 ÷ 3 = 2

27 ÷ 3 = 9

18 ÷ 3 = 6

HOME ACTIVITY **20**

Divide 20 by 4. **5**

32 divided by 4. **8**

One quarter of 16 **4**

36 ÷ 4 = **9**

4 ÷ 4 = **1**

40 ÷ 4 = **10**

24 ÷ 4 = **6**

Colour answers blue.

28 ÷ 4 = **7**

0 ÷ 4 = **0**

12 ÷ 4 = **3**

8 ÷ 4 = **2**

Colour answers red.

Colour answers green.

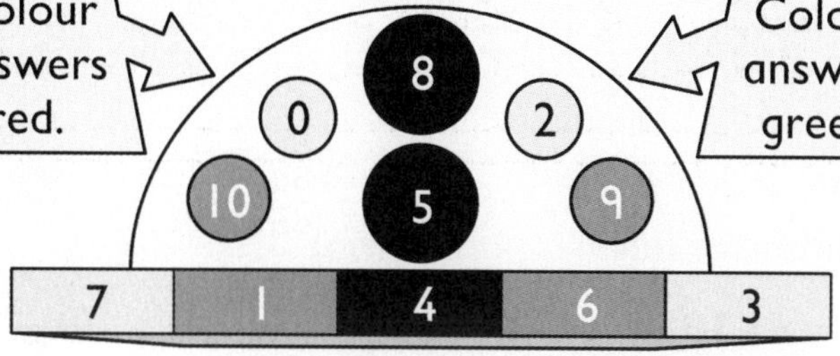

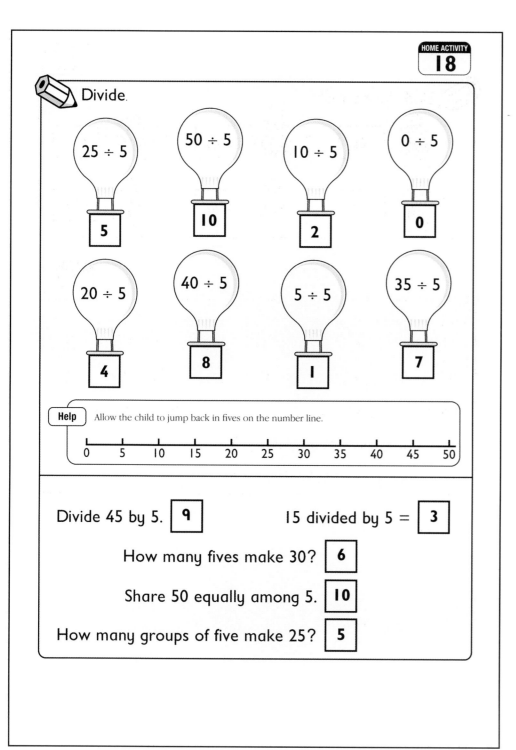

HOME ACTIVITY 21

Share 35 equally among 5.	**7**	16 divided by 2	**8**
How many tens make 60?	**6**	Divide 24 by 4.	**6**
One quarter of 36	**9**	Half of 14	**7**

$20 \div 5 =$ **4** $18 \div 3 =$ **6** $100 \div 10 =$ **10**

$0 \div 4 =$ **0** $30 \div 5 =$ **6** $15 \div 3 =$ **5**

40 $\div 10 = 4$ **30** $\div 3 = 10$ **18** $\div 2 = 9$

HOME ACTIVITY 22

Write each amount in **pounds** and **pence**.

£2·57   **£3·03**   **£0·85**

Write each amount in **pence**.

£3·20   £4·06   £0·68

320p   **406p**   **68p**

How much does Tim have left?

£1.10

HOME ACTIVITY 23

How much?

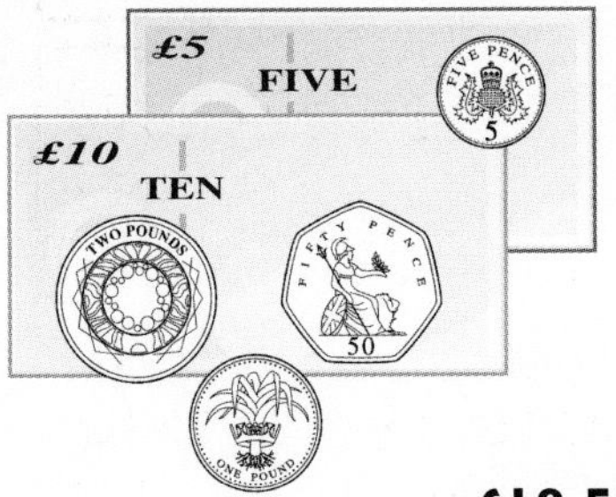

£18·55

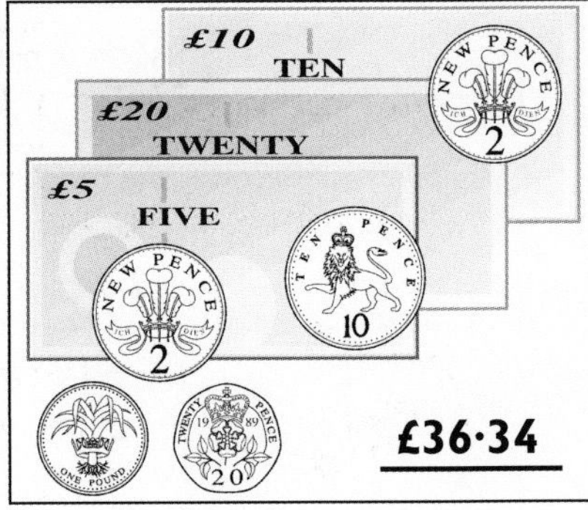

£36·34

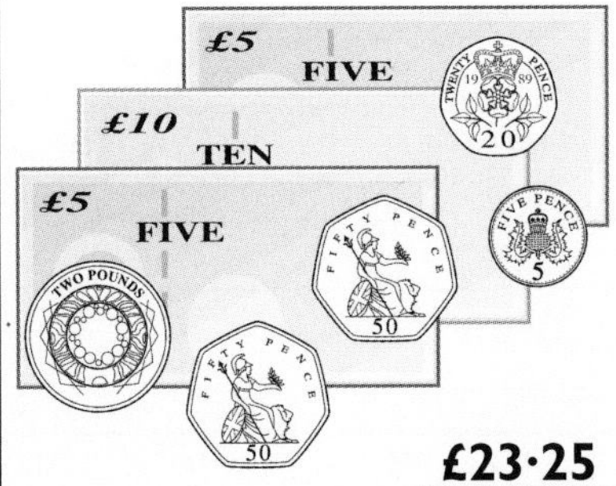

£23·25

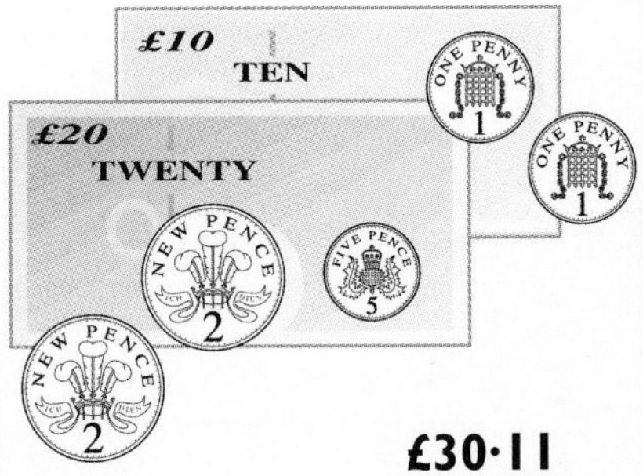

£30·11

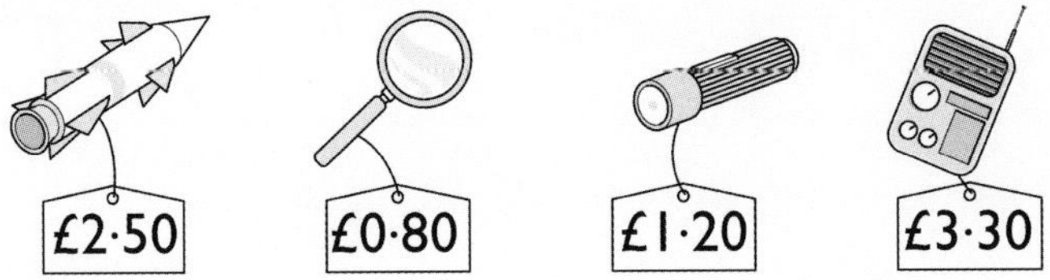

Find the cost of

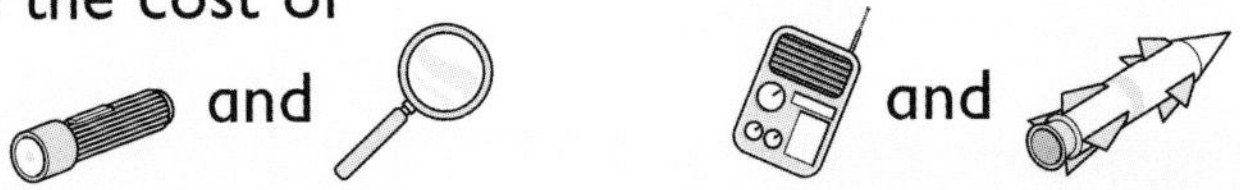

£2.00   **£5.80**

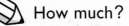

HOME ACTIVITY
24

one tenth of 50 = 5

one tenth of 80 = 8

one tenth of 10 = 1

$\frac{1}{10}$ of 20 = 2

$\frac{1}{10}$ of 100 = 10

$\frac{1}{10}$ of 70 = 7

There are 90 counters in the bag.
One tenth of them are red.
How many are **not** red? 81

Help To find one tenth of, for example 50, the child could:
– divide 50 by 10 or
– think 'Ten times what make fifty?'

HOME ACTIVITY
25

Colour

one third

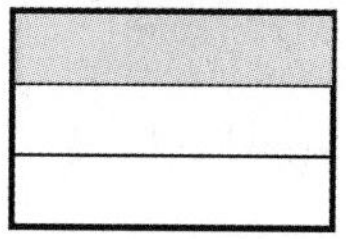

two thirds

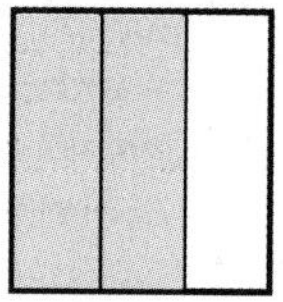

three thirds

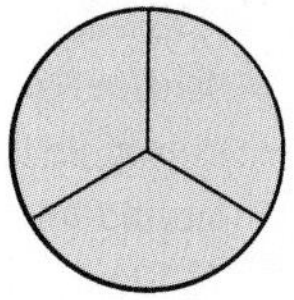

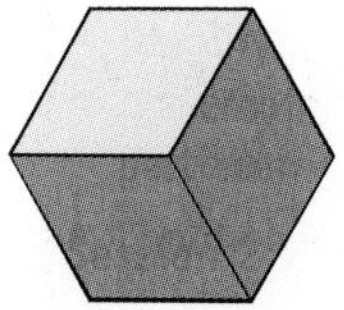

one third red
two thirds blue.

What fraction is **not** shaded?

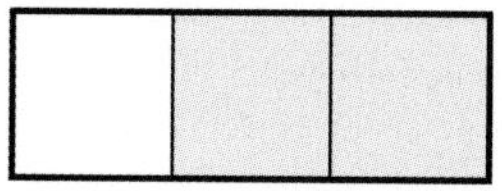

$\frac{1}{3}$

Tick (✓) the shapes which show fifths.

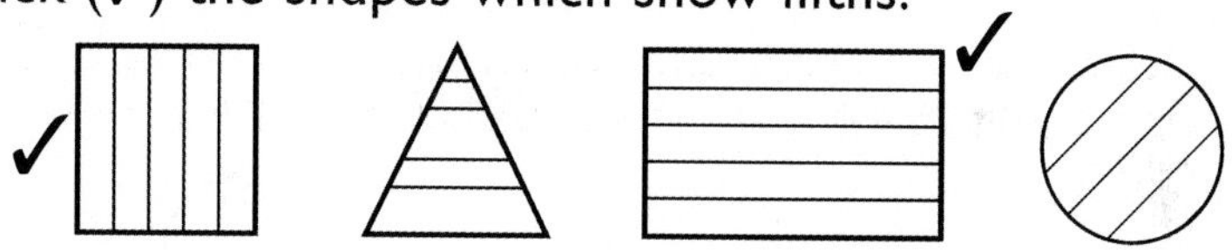

Colour

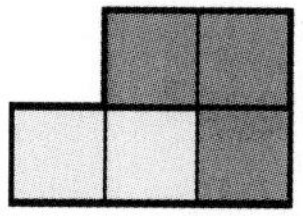

three fifths red
two fifths yellow

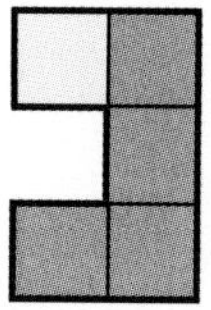

one fifth red
four fifths blue.

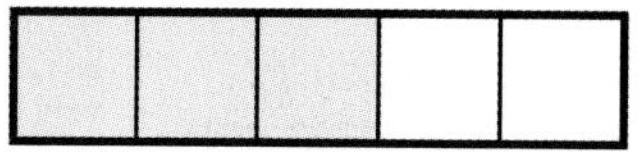

What fraction is

- shaded $\frac{3}{5}$
- not shaded? $\frac{2}{5}$

HOME ACTIVITY **26**

Write each time using **minutes past** or **minutes to**.

5 minutes past 11

20 minutes to 4

The time on this clock is **4.35**

Write each of these times.

11.55

10.25

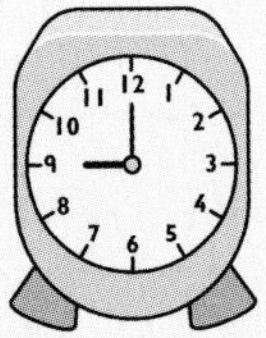

9.00

Quarter past 8. **8.15**

10 minutes to 5. **4.50**

20 minutes past 7. **7.20**

Quarter to 11. **10.45**

HOME ACTIVITY **27**

How long?

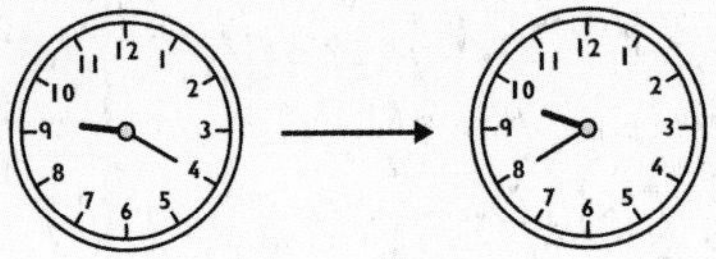

20 minutes

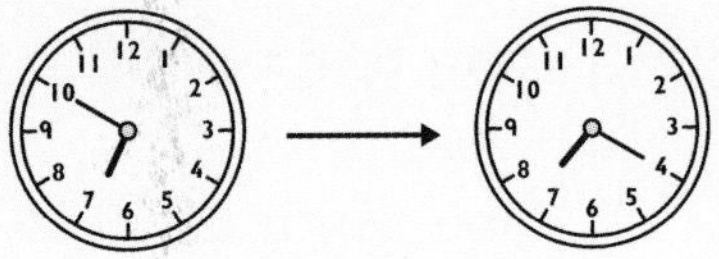

30 minutes

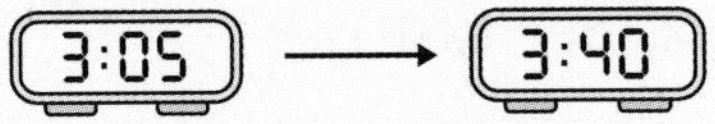

35 minutes

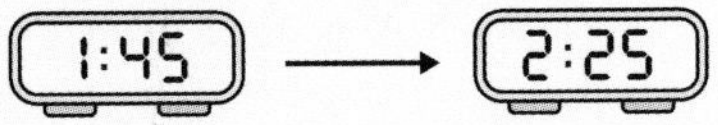

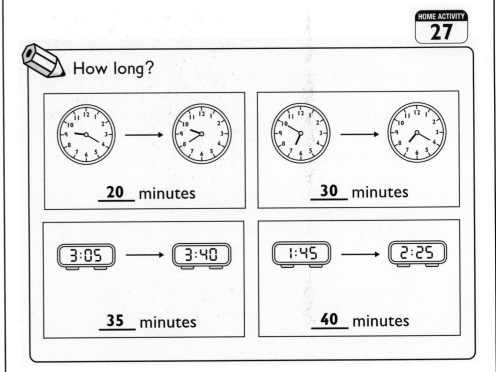

40 minutes